INTRODUCTION

In my years as Executive Editor of The Republican, many columnists, local, regional, and national came and went. One stood out among all others.

Theo Chipkin's first column was about banning dogs from Longmeadow's outdoor eating establishments. Theo fought for the rights of dogs as he should since Theo was a dog.

His first two columns created quite a stir. It was clearly time to give this puppy his chance at fame and maybe help sell newspapers. I okayed the column which lasted for six years.

Theo made his mark in a lot of places. This dog had his day and we were better for it.

Thanks Theo. We know you have probably heard about your book as the first canine journalist while looking down from dog heaven.

By Wayne E. Phaneuf
Executive Editor Emeritus

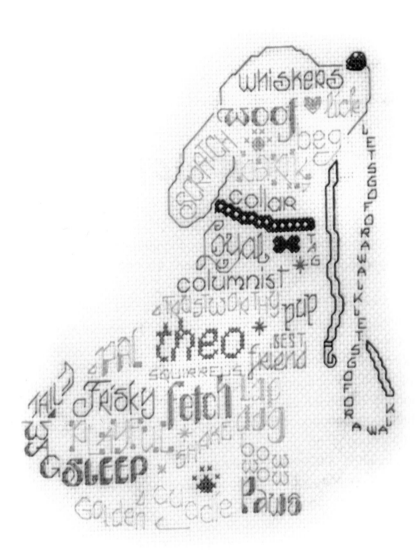

Needlepoint by Nancy Murinka.

FOREWORD

In tribute to the true voice of this book, I guess I will start at the end of my tale, then in a roundabout way chase it forward.

What started as a howl of protest over being barred from the outside (yes, outside) of a local coffee establishment morphed into a newspaper and Internet column in which I attempted to climb into Theo's golden skin and present the world from his special perspective -- both four feet on, and four feet off the ground.

By the time the column ceased publication six years later, Theo had had his say more than 200 times, extemporizing on subjects ranging from his futile attempts to catch squirrels to the ethically problematic question of who exactly was leashed to whom.

Theo philosophized over his favorite season (he liked fall the best, so many leaves to jump through) and observed stoically as his own golden hair turned at first cream and at last to white, while still thankful that his somewhat dim memory kept him firmly centered in the here and now.

If the two of us weren't exactly famous, then we were at least locally well-known and his small bit of notoriety nicely coincided with his glad-to-meet-you nature so that utter strangers who spotted us on our daily perambulations through the local city parks and neighborhoods were prompted to remark unabashedly "he's beautiful."

And they never meant me.

Still, I adjusted to my sidekick role the way a parent will step aside to make room for a child's accomplishments. As he was blessed with a sense of time that didn't extend past dinner, it was mostly me who thought that the two of us had plenty of time in our golden years to work on our memoirs together.

It turns out we didn't.

Theo died shortly after his column ended, following a brief struggle with canine lymphoma, which he endured with the kind of stoic equanimity that was all the more heartbreaking to watch after a lifetime of good health (the human idiom of being "sick as a dog" never made much sense to him.) It seemed that after nearly 10 years of circling his dog dish like clockwork, then consuming dinner before it even reached the bottom of his bowl that even he was surprised at his sudden lack of appetite. And although he maintained his "count me in" response to any family excursion, we could see that while the spirit remained willing, the body was giving out.

A visit to the vet confirmed what we already feared and while we were consoled with her wise counsel that our animals are always on loan to us, it hardly eased the pain that this particular loan was about to come due.

On our family vacation to the New Jersey shore, Theo rallied along with us at the thought of sand, sea and perhaps a bit of ice cream, then gamely jumped into the back seat even as we feared that for him, this would be a one-way trip. Our vet, who cleared the trip with the comment that sometimes a change of scenery surrounded by loved ones might do some good, said that when his time came, he would let us know.

And he did.

We were heartbroken as only those who have lost a beloved animal companion can know and we have appreciated the comfort and thoughtfulness of all those who knew Theo, or through his column recognized the universality of what a dog can add to a household.

To the question of whether we might get another animal we at first responded - as so many bereaved pet owners do - "of course we won't; of course we will; and maybe someday."

What we hadn't counted on was the emptiness of the house without Theo. Less than a year later, our someday arrived in the form of a golden retriever puppy that we named Reilly. While we love him unreservedly, we know that there will never be another Theo.

We comfort ourselves with our memories and the knowledge that we fulfilled our promise to give Theo the best life we possibly could.

He certainly did the same for us.

By Robert Chipkin

TABLE OF CONTENTS

Catalogues. Catalogue shopping is to my taste
Vet. It's not personal, but vets make me nervous
Dog class. If it's Wednesday; it's dog class
AKC. The American Kennel Club has once again listed its prize dog, and it's not me.
Bronze again. There's no shame in third place; but it's not first.

Another birthday. The years slip away
Birthday parties. I'm a party animal
Step. I've lost a step
Gray. I'm going gray
Weight. I am the biggest loser
Balto. I've got to face it, I'll never be Balto
Time. It's so confusing
Beyond. I'd rather think of the hereafter, hereafter.
Journey. The journey is a trip
Lost. The saddest words; lost dog
Photo. Humans are fascinated with photos; I'd rather play
Camera shy. I'm not picture perfect

Foxes. Friendly foxes? I don't think so.
Squirrels. Squirrels have never been happy to see me; I don't know why
Owls. Owls can really turn heads
Ticks. I hate ticks; there I've said it
Skunks. Getting skunked stinks
Smart. Dogs are smarter than cats; but I knew that
Love cats. Dogs love you more than cats; but I knew that too
Cat in the Hat. Fictional cats are my favorite
Uncle. Congratulations; today I am an uncle
Vizsla. I veesh I vas a Vizsla

Health provider. Make someone happy and you'll be a dog
Therapy. A good dog is the best therapy
Comfort. Comfort dogs offer comfort

Baby. A baby visits; but what's the fuss?
Guests. Dog guests come; but even better, they go
Sidekick. I'd rather work alone
Professor. I can teach some new tricks
Kitchen. Kitchen workers get guest treatment
Wedding. Here comes the bride; there goes the dog

Year of the dog. This is my year
Winter. Winter's chill warms my heart
Winter again. I love the season I'm in
Beach. Life's a beach
Vacations. Vacations, c'est moi
Thanksgiving. A holiday that makes sense
Calendar. Every day is a dog day

GETTING STARTED

MY COLUMNIST DEBUT

Ever since my journalism debut last week, barking about a recently enforced ordinance keeping me sitting outside Starbucks while my master (actually I hate that word, dogs know it's the other way around) gets caffeinated, people have been asking how it feels to be columnist.

Note I say people have been asking. Dogs couldn't care less. Put me next to Lassie and I'd sniff her the same as I do any other lassie. Rin Tin Tin (whoever came up with that name?) would get the usual run, run runaround and then we'd both be on our way. And believe me it won't work out well for any Hollywood dog who likes to show off how smart he is (most dogs keep that to themselves). By fall, he'll be doing Alpo commercials.

And as for the burning issue of dogs outside Starbucks I've said my piece. It was never about me anyway. Frankly, I'd much rather be walking through the woods, getting my paws muddy and chasing squirrels. My whole point was that after my owner does all that, sometimes he likes a coffee and I don't mind it when pretty girls come up and pet me and say "he's beautiful" (note to owner: They always mean me). It seems like outside Starbucks is the place for that.

But that's just my opinion. It's not like the right to drink-coffee-with-your-dog-outside-Starbucks is in the Constitution. And just because I thought the whole hoo-hah was a problem in search of a solution doesn't mean I couldn't be wrong.

Live and let live, I say. Dogs are like that.

But people apparently, aren't.

The response to my musings was -- like the breed of many of my best friends -- mixed.

It took a while to get used to this. Dogs are used to praise, criticism does not become them. That's why you so rarely hear anything about dogs dissing other dogs outside nightclubs, or punching paparazzi, or having messy affairs which end in multi-million divorce settlements. When was the last time a dog made the cover of a supermarket tabloid? I even feel bad about that Alpo dig I made a few paragraphs back.

It's our natural goodness that makes us so thin-skinned about criticism. So imagine my surprise when my take-it-or-leave it Starbucks opinion caused the internet to practically burn up (can it do that? We dogs don't get the internet) with comments, some of it very undoglike.

For example, one writer who shall remain nameless (apparently they're all nameless on the internet) suggested I might use the Starbucks as a bathroom.

Let me say I would never do that. I don't even use the bathroom as a bathroom. I do my business in the deep woods where it becomes part of the great circle of life or politely in my yard where my owner dutifully picks up after me. And taking a look at the way most of the other Starbucks customers run to the bathroom the minute they finish their coffee, I'd put up my prostate against theirs anytime.

Others says they're allergic (whose problem is that?) or that we're dirty (puleese, if you could smell what we smell), or that they just don't like dogs (outright dogism I say) .

My owner, who has some experience in these matters, says I should take the criticism in stride. He says that the response to about half the columns he writes can be summed up in two words:

"You suck."

My owner says that the comments, even the negative ones, are all positive in a way, since they show readership.

As I said, I don't care.

But my mother always taught me that if you don't have anything nice to say, don't say anything.

Actually, I barely knew my mother. I just made that up.

Columnists, I've heard, do that.

PATIO POLITICS

It appears that the people have spoken, which I'll admit is not as much of a man-bites-dog story as it sounds until you realize that what they have spoken about is me, and my future as what I humbly believe to be the first regularly appearing dog columnist in America.

For late arrivals, my journalistic career began unceremoniously when the members of the Longmeadow health board decided to enforce a seldomly followed ordinance barring dogs from outside eating establishments, and me specifically from outside Starbucks, where I thought I was actually adding to the boulevard ambience of the parking lot view by simply being charming.

I naturally assumed that the health board would see the error of their ways and repeal this dreadful bit of dogism, perhaps offering to make it up to me and all dogs with a special Theo Day (frappacinos half price) and who knows, maybe a small statue.

Yet curiously, they held their ground which would have been the end of it as far as I was concerned, since: a) I don't drink coffee, and b) dogs have much better things to do than to pick up after the mistakes of humans.

What was surprising however was the avalanche of emails sent in care of my master from loyal readers pointing out the refreshing nature of canine journalism and asking for more of my opinions on things like presidential politics and the future of the European Union. On one level of course, this is preposterous since dogs are notoriously poor writers (it's that opposable thumb thing) and don't care much for reading as most of the literature aimed at us rather pointedly comes down to some version of "no dogs allowed."

Nor do we hold much in the way of opinions since face it, we pretty much go where our masters tell us, and since our basic philosophy is to follow our nose, it doesn't much matter which way that nose is headed.

Still the reviews kept pouring in calling me insightful, creative, refreshing and, in one reader's words (and I am not making this up), smarter than George Will, which I guess is a compliment, even though I've never met the dog.

Not all this praise was properly appreciated. My master for example, who considers himself a columnist in his own right, was a bit peeved that my favorable comments exceeded his by a hefty margin, and not one made any unsavory remarks about my ancestry or intelligence. Nor was he particularly pleased to be stopped in the woods on a recent walk only to be asked what it felt like to be less popular than a dog.

But then again, most humans are.

It was also nice to hear (and again I am not making this up) that several of my correspondents suggested I get a raise.

Of course dogs don't really care about money. What would we spend it on? We eat the same thing every day. We don't wear clothes. Travel agents frown upon us, and - not to bring up old wounds - Starbucks apparently doesn't want our business.

Nor do we care about fame. Our instinct around paparazzi is about the same as Alex Baldwin's - it makes us feel like biting. And since we don't get married or divorced, fan magazines rarely give us a sniff.

Still it's nice to know that someone cares and in that spirit I promise to do something that no other columnist - human or canine - in the history of journalism has ever done.

If I don't have anything worthwhile to say, I won't say anything.

So you won't see anything here about politics, world affairs or the fluctuating dollar. Don't know, don't care, won't say.

But if you want to know how we cavort through the forest without tripping over our back feet, or why we keep chasing squirrels long after we know we'll never catch one, I'm your dog.

See you around the woods.

FAN

Not many humans know it, but I am a huge baseball fan and it's not only because I am named after Theo Nathaniel Epstein (or perhaps, he is named after me since technically in dog years I am quite a bit his senior.)

For those who have been living in a cave (nothing wrong with cave dwelling which was quite good enough for my lupine ancestors) Theo Epstein became the youngest general manager in the history of Major League Baseball when the Boston Red Sox hired him in 2002 at the age of 28, presenting him with the impossible dream of overcoming the team's cursed ineptitude, a feat he accomplished two years later by bringing the World Series trophy to Boston where fans had been waiting patiently for a championship for only 86 human years.

So it seemed only fitting when I joined my New England household some years later that my mistress - a die-hard Red Sox fan - would name me "Theo," (a much better choice than Nathaniel or Epstein which would have exposed me to quite a bit of teasing around the dog park.)

So you can see my baseball roots run deep. Even without my MLB namesake, it was clear from an early age that I was a natural boy of summer. It didn't take long for me to realize that fielding was only a human name for "retrieving," and that four legs can be quite an advantage when tracking down fly balls (not that there's anything wrong with flies).

While I will make a game try to fetch just about anything, baseballs are by far my favorite, as tennis balls are a trifle squishy and tracking down a basketball or soccer ball is really biting off a bit more than I can politely chew.

On the other hand (as if I had hands) a baseball is just the right size and consistency for a retriever to sink his teeth into however they are pitched.

Fastballs don't faze me, I am seldom fooled by the curve and the spitter seems only natural to me as I've seldom encountered anything that isn't improved by a bit of healthy drool.

I'm not much of a hitter, but I certainly love to walk which you would think would make me an asset to any team. And yet curiously, I remain undrafted.

Well never mind, I enjoy being a fan, since my love of baseballs extends naturally to baseball teams. And I am fortunate to live in New England where a long standing attraction to socks dovetails (nothing wrong with doves or tails) quite naturally with the team's moniker.

In fact there are few things better than spending a lazy summer afternoon on the couch, sock in mouth, watching the Red Sox retrieve just about everything that comes their way.

In this I am especially fortunate as it would be quite hard to warm up to a team named the Marlins, the Cubs, the Blue Jays, the Orioles, or heaven forbid the Tigers (small cats are unknowable, but large ones are just plain scary) all begging the question of why baseball teams are never named after dogs.

I suppose there might be something better than to be a Red Sox fan named Theo with the dog days coming and the team on a hot streak.

But honestly, I can't think of what that might be.

CALL ME THEO

I realize, put that way, it sounds like the opening line of the world's most famous whale tale, which brings up a small question of its own.

Why would a whale need a name anyway? It's not like anyone calls him to dinner, or asks him to fetch. Whales don't really do tricks, unless you count the occasional head-on sinking of a whale boat, which, if you ask me, is certainly justifiable since the entire purpose of a whale boat is to KILL WHALES, and with a mission like that, you can't expect the whales to cheer your arrival.

So it seems to me that whales hardly need names at all, let alone one called Moby (which, like Dopey, sounds to me like a name more befitting a Disney dwarf than a whale.)

But when you're a dog, a name is quite useful and seems to be universally expected, as evidenced by the first thing a stranger asks (after remarking on my general beauteousness) - "What's his name?"

Now, on the farm where I was born, I didn't have a name as the proprietor made it her policy not to name the pups because, she said, if she did, she could never part with them.

But what I didn't know at the time was that I actually had a name long before I got to my new home. Years before my mistress acquired me, she decided that whenever she did get a dog, she would name it Theo, after Theo Epstein, the former Boston Red Sox general manager who helped guide the team to its first World Series championship in a century.

She figured that if she didn't name me for the architect of that miracle season she might have to wait another 100 years (700 dog years) for the chance, which would require inordinant patience, even for a Red Sox fan. And as it turns out, she wasn't far from wrong.

Theo Epstein is now in Chicago, the Red Sox finished in last place and (I am not making this up) complete strangers have come up to my mistress and asked if she has ever considered changing my name.

I guess you never know how names will turn out.

I like my name. It sounds strong without being too formal. I once knew a dog named Ranagut Dune III out of Delegate Kennels, which sounded pretty high-faluting for a dog. Everyone wound up calling him Deli and lots of folks thought he was born in the back of a cold cuts factory.

Serves his master right.

Technically, my last name is Chipkin, but I don't use it much. It's necessary, I suppose, at the vet's office to keep my records straight and at City Hall where I'm licensed (A license for a dog? Don't get me started.) But just about everywhere else, I'm just Theo, which suits me fine.

It seems to me that last names are more trouble than they're worth. Before you know it, you have a Social Security number and a PIN and you start getting electricity bills and notices from the IRS and a free month's trial of a home security system. Why would I need that? As near I can figure out, *I* am the home security system.

I did get a credit card offer once, no annual fee and a low introductory rate. But I declined. Dogs are impulsive by nature, and anything that promises you can get something now and pay for it later sounds like a very dangerous idea.

So now when the mail comes, my master gets all the bills and the postman gives me a dog biscuit.

Who's got the better deal? You decide.

Inset photo by Dale Ruff.

I HEAR IT'S MY BIRTHDAY

The truth is, I don't really remember much about my birth, but then again who does? When it comes right down to it, aren't all birthday stories at bottom somebody else's version of something we can't recall. It's not until much later that we look back upon our grown-up selves and wonder, just where we came from.

In my case it's a farm in Rhode Island, where I've been told I was one of three pups born to Gunner and Chloe. All accounts are that my dad was a handsome dog (I don't doubt it) and my mom kept quite busy herding my two brothers and sister around like cats as we frolicked over hill and dale getting used to what we thought would be our home forever.

Alas, home doesn't stay home for long on a farm, and breeders don't have the luxury of maintaining nuclear families. My breeder said she doesn't even name her puppies because if she did, she could never let them go. And letting go is what breeders do. Luckily, my master already knew that if ever she got a dog, his name would be Theo, after Theo Epstein, the general manager of the Red Sox who ended the World Series curse. I don't believe in curses and Theo Epstein has departed the Red Sox and is off trying to end a curse somewhere else. But I like my name, so in that way it was all really a blessing, Red Sox fan or not.

In any event, I had the rare puppy luck of leaving the farm with my brother who was bought at the same time by my master's sister.

Sisters getting brothers. I like that part of my birthday story.

The dog tale goes even farther back than that. It seems that my master never gave in to the persistent requests of her three young children to get a dog.

"You don't need a dog," she always said with the staunch encouragement of her husband, who had a pretty good idea that his place in the family pecking order could only be diminished by adding a canine. "You have sisters."

Even better, she had a sister, their aunt, who lived nearby and had a golden retriever, Casey, who served faithfully as the family dog as the kids grew up.

And that would have suited everyone just fine until the family dog met an untimely death just before the holidays leaving everyone so bereft that that Christmas will forever be known as "the year we lost Casey."

In fact, the grief was so great that my master's sister vowed she just couldn't stand to get another dog until she realized soon after that she couldn't stand not to.

And so mostly as moral support my master went dog shopping at the farm in Rhode Island and lo and behold the sisters came back with brothers.

And that is the rest of the story.

So around Christmas each year the families gather and quietly celebrate the day that my brother, Brady, and I joined the sisters and the kids and we became a "blended family." Sort of like the Partridge Family, except of course, we're dogs.

Now I know that many humans don't like revealing their age, but I don't mind. I'm three, which I've been told in people years is really 21, although I can't figure why any self-respecting dog would want to know how old he was in people years when he is most definitely a dog. It's like saying a person who is 40 is only 20 in elephant years. Who, other than an aging Hollywood starlet reduced to playing opposite Dumbo, would say that?

Still, if the sisters insist upon celebrating the brothers' birthday, we really don't mind. We get silly doggy toys that we tear apart searching for the squeaky bladder inside, and snappy matching bandanas that we wear twice before chewing them to ribbons. We hear bad dog jokes from the relative who shows up faithfully bearing what he calls our new leash on life, and we've been known to don goofy hats that make us look decidedly undoglike.

If we're cute enough (and we always are) we get a piece of cake that is in strict violation of the no begging rules that are enforced vigorously the rest of the year.

For our masters it's a special day. For us it's no big deal because when you're a dog every day is special.

Still, it makes them happy and so we're happy.

Dogs are like that.

Happy birthday to us.

See you around the cake scraps.

I HEAR IT'S HER BIRTHDAY

My master celebrated her birthday recently, just a few months after careful readers will recall that I celebrated mine and I must say I much prefer my version.

My birthday included some snappy new dog toys, which I made short work of in search of the most interesting part which as any dog knows is the squeaky bladder that lies within; a Red Sox bandana which I chewed to ribbons in honor of their abysmal past season, (I am named Theo and take my fan status seriously even though my namesake has departed to an even more hapless team) and a general suspension of the no begging rule which included some tasty birthday cake and an extra portion of dog treats.

All in all, a very good day.

My master's birthday on the other hand consisted of a month of general fretting about the upcoming day, a noticeable uptick in the aches and pains quotient she expressed to me on our daily walks, and a seasonal malaise (an emotion completely foreign to dogs) that accompanied her misfortune of having a birthday in the dead of winter.

Not that I didn't try to console her (one of my strongest points). I reminded her that dogs do a very good job of living outside time, even though humans keep reminding us that one dog year is like seven of theirs, a subject that polite dogs would never bring up if the shoe were on the other paw. Not that the math, with its implicit message that we are likely to get to the end of the road before them depresses us. Anyone who has ever unleashed us knows that we always get to the end of the road first.

We just don't care.

Now if it were me, I'd spend my birthday romping in the woods, futilely chasing squirrels and following my nose wherever it led me. And if that doesn't sound like a special way to spend your birthday, you are missing the point that for a dog every day is a special day, which I might add is a pretty good philosophy to live by, birthday or not.

But my master, to her credit chose to celebrate her birthday by surrounding herself with friends, which is a pretty good second choice if your romping days are behind you and singing doggerel songs (my favorite) in which many words seemed to rhyme with "Depends" but whose general theme as I took it was that although Aging's Hell (sung endlessly and slightly out of meter to the tune of "Silver Bells") the sole comfort was that at least everyone was going through it together.

The guest speaker (me of course) added some self-serving praise about my master's best qualities (forgiving of faults, never too busy to cuddle, and a strong tolerance for doggy breath) and some canine wisdom about living in the moment, viewing a short memory as a virtue, and adoring others as you would like to be adored.

In other words be a dog.

Or if that's not possible, just think like one, and act accordingly.

All in all, when the guests had gone home and dishes cleared (I helped with the usual prewash by licking the plates) I like to think that I made her birthday just a little brighter, just as she had for me.

After all, we're in this together,

WOLF

As any politician knows, dig deep enough into any family closet and you're likely to find a skeleton (not that there's anything wrong with digging or skeletons – love them bones.)

So I'm not afraid to admit that behind my outward bonhomie and congenial exterior lies an inescapable fact.

I am part wolf.

Not the part before your eyes of course that is unflinchingly loyal, unfailingly kind and a steadfast friend to all, but the part buried deep in my DNA hearkening back thousands of years to a time when my dinner arrived not by supper dish, but by the call of the wild and the thrill of the hunt.

Not that I have anything to hide of course. I'm proud of my roots (I've even chewed on some of them) and I take a certain rakish pleasure in recalling a history of hunting in packs and howling at the moon, rather like the way I imagine office-bound humans must feel when learning that they are related to sea-faring pirates.

Who among humans doesn't occasionally look in the mirror and yearn just a bit for some more swash in their buckle, and what canine doesn't secretly long to be a little less lady and a little more tramp?

I must say that after the most elementary internet search into my roots, my master looked at me with a bit more respect upon learning that I am descended from a breed of feisty hunters who over the centuries came to realize that with a modest application of God-given charm, could domesticate humans enough to simply give us food instead of us having to go out in the forest and hunt for it.

And that from a single species of gray wolf, we have now evolved into 400 recognizable breeds including the Australian dingo (best known for its use as an aborigine bed warmer), the Mexican Xola, the Japanese Aleita, the King

Charles spaniel, and my personal favorite, the New Guinean singing dog.

More dog fun facts: We have 18 muscles around our ears so that we can tilt, raise and rotate our heads at the mere mention of the letters W-A-L-K and that our nose has 25 times the olfactory receptors than even the most smelly (and I don't mean that negatively) human.

Our patron saint is Saint Hubert, (656-727) which has little to do with Saint Bernards, who are actually named after a monastery; and the ancient Greeks featured us prominently in the temple of the god Asklepisos where we were often called upon to heal the sick by – get this -- licking them.

Our military record is exemplary including a canine parachute corps dropped behind enemy lines in World War II to sniff out booby traps and navigate mine fields; and a collie named Max who holds the record for the most raids, man or dog, behind German lines.

There is more of course, but our modesty along with the fact that we can't really talk prevents us from bragging (did I mention, that we were the first in space, Soviet Sputnik 7, 1957. Look it up.)

Better to simply remind our masters that the day we gave up the pack to live among humans changed history for all of us, and to never lose sight of the simple truth that "To understand dogs, consider wolves."

PC... WHAT'S IN A PET NAME

Although we dogs like to think of ourselves as just as sensitive as any of God's creatures, I must say that we don't spend much time worrying about being politically correct.

After all since we don't really talk, we generally don't have to think about choosing our words which keeps us out of a boatload of trouble since we are seldom misunderstood.

Most of the time our nonverbal communication works just swell. We circle the dog dish and dinner is never far behind. We scratch the door and pretty soon the door opens. We seldom have to say "or else" because just about everyone in the house knows what else usually follows if we don't get the proper response.

And most of the time our live and let live philosophy prevents us from taking offense. Most humans think we're beautiful anyway but even if they didn't we wouldn't go all hang-dog about it. It's not like I have an opinion about whether a retriever is any better-looking than a Labrador, or an Irish setter. And I would never call another dog fat even if he did look like he spent a little too long around the dog dish. We are what we are and that's pretty much that.

At the end of the day, we're all dogs.

But humans use words and find all sorts of ways to get themselves into trouble even when they don't mean any harm at all. My master tells me that when he was growing up an entire generation of women were called girls well past their 13th birthday and just about all the unmarried women he knew were called Miss and didn't even know they were supposed to be offended until Ms. PC came along and told them they should be angry.

Not to mention that some things that people take umbrage at are plain old true. Frankly I've never minded being called a son-of-a-you-know-what because when you come right down to it, that's what I am. And when someone calls me a sly old dog for cadging an extra treat even though it's near dinner, they're usually right.

It would be as if I were to learn that I should be insulted to be called a dog and should henceforth be referred to only as a Canis lupis familiaris. Would I suddenly be any happier? I doubt it. Still, I'm sure the PC crowd had good reasons to be offended at the things they were offended by and if someone wanted to be called something else I guess it would be OK with me. After all as Shakespeare's dog once said "a dog by any other name would smell as sweet, even if he spent most of the day chasing skunks."

All of which is a roundabout way of expressing my surprise upon learning from a correspondent (I never even had correspondents until I became a columnist and frankly I didn't miss them) that I was offending myself every time I thought of my master as well, my master.

"Can't you see how that plays into the subject-object-anthro-centric view of the world" she asked in full dudgeon. "Just the thought of being mastered is so…demeaning. After all if he's the master what does that make you….a pet?"

Well, I suppose.

Now I am seldom in full dudgeon. Just the thought of it makes me want to take a nap. And I guess I've always made peace with the fact that dogs aren't really in charge around here. I mean we don't vote, or drive or make foreign policy. But I had to admit that maybe she had a point especially when she suggested a politically correct alternative to the master-pet relationship. "You my dear Theo are no pet, and he is certainly no master," she went on. Henceforth he is to be referred as only your person, or better yet, your human. And you are his client. And the two of you are forever to be considered, co-owners.

So that apparently is that. Frankly I expected to feel better about all this now that we had gotten our nomenclature down but it seems that life has gone on pretty much as before. I still circle the dish and scratch the door, he still opens the door and fills the dish.

Who's in charge?

You decide. And if you ever see me in the park feel free to tell me. I'll be the one walking my human.

CELEBRITY STATUS

Photo by Mark Murray.

TV DEBUT

There's just about no way that a dog can prepare for his TV debut.

A dog lives a simple life and needs just about no preparation for daily living. No one ever taught me to chase squirrels. I see them and I'm gone. The truth is that I don't even know why I'm chasing them, and it doesn't really matter. I chase, therefore I am.

Ditto for playing with sticks. If I had an opposable thumb (which humans are so proud of, but frankly I think is more trouble than it's worth) I suppose I could think of lots of things to do with a stick. I could build a home (not that it worked out so well for that little pig. The truth is, you might think your home is sturdy, but sooner or later the wolf comes to your door). Or use it to start a fire (ask Bambi how well that works out). Or perhaps conduct an orchestra (artistic types are so temperamental). But I'd rather just play with the stick and be done with it.

Works great. No preparation needed.

Preparation is a two-edged sword. You sacrifice the present for the future and you're always one step away from worry, which is about the most undoglike characteristic I can imagine. I suppose it is a way to accomplish things, but most accomplishments are highly overrated. The one thing for certain about two-edged swords is that they pretty much cut you either way.

Anyway, the point is that for most things, I find that I am prepared enough, which in a dog's world is high praise. In my master's family his mother always said that all the girls were "pretty enough," which was always offered as a compliment although just about no one ever took it that way. It meant that their looks were sufficient to garner notice and a likely mate but not enough to go to their heads and make them too high-falutin' - whatever that meant, but it was no great honor. I have a feeling that my mother, if I ever met her, would say that I am prepared enough to be a dog.

Theo Chipkin, center, with his agent, Robert Chipkin, and host Carrie Saldo on the set of "Connecting Point" at the WGBY-TV, Channel 57 studios in Springfield.

Still, none of that prepares a dog for television.

So when, as a consequence of my newfound status as the only regularly appearing canine columnist in America, television came calling, I really had no idea what to expect.

The actual invitation came by email (which I am still getting the hang of) courtesy of Jim Madigan, director of public affairs programs for WGBY-TV, Channel 57, who spends much of his time interviewing politicians but who nevertheless had a "nose for news" (I on the other hand have a nose for everything) and reasoned that his viewers might be willing to stop worrying about the election or the economy long enough to care about what a dog thought about, well, being a dog.

And so I found myself in the WGBY studios on Hampden Street in Springfield generally being fussed over and beautified (no problem there) while host Carrie Saldo prepped my master on what to expect. It turns out, of course, that he was no better prepared for what questions one might ask a dog than I was, the only difference was that he was worried.

I don't worry, but I can be unpredictable. I'm not one of those Hollywood canines who has been brought up from birth to mug for the camera and who has been bribed by endless treats and trained by dog whisperers (why are they whispering anyway) to sit quietly while human actors try to remember their lines. When I get bored, I fidget. When I get hungry, I look for my dog bowl. When I have gas ... well, you get the picture.

I'm sure everyone concerned was hoping none of that would happen, but the truth is no one knows how I will act from moment to moment, least of all me.

Dogs are just that way. We improvise.

And that's just what I did through the usual questions of my parentage, how I came to Springfield, my foray into politics championing the rights of canines to sit quietly outside Starbucks (a tempest in a coffeepot if you ask me) and the response to my columns so far (enthusiastic, but I've yet to hear from the Pulitzer judges.)

I flirted with the host, mugged for the cameraman and pretty much ignored the director, which, I understand, is par for the course for "the talent," which is how I was referred to and which I did not dispute.

At the end of the interview, I was invited to come back soon, which is TV talk for either "I really mean it" or "not on your life," but I'm not sure which.

So, how did I do?

Well, I guess the viewers will decide.

Hopefully I gave them something to think about, and if not, I have a thick skin. I was born that way.

In the final analysis, I figure that if I wasn't good, then I certainly was good enough.

Artist Patricia Coon stands before her portrait of Theo at the Paragon Art Gallery in Easthampton.

ART SHOW

Dogs aren't often invited to art openings and I must say for the most part we don't miss them much.

I rarely sip chardonnay, (or sip anything for that matter; I mostly slurp) and vegetable crudités leave me cold. I can't say I would mind munching tiny cheese cubes but doing so while being expected to make polite conversation on the state of the arts is just a bit above my pay grade. The truth is, my position on modern art is eclectic — I eat everything.

And so I was surprised, flattered really, to hear from Patricia Coon recently who said that she had admired me from afar (most people just come up and pet me) and that she had taken the liberty of painting my portrait from the photo that accompanies this column. Would I do her the honor of coming to the portrait's unveiling at the Paragon Arts Gallery in Easthampton as part of the 2nd annual Holiday Sales Extravaganza, Dakin-Pioneer-Valley-Humane-Society, Fund-raiser in Easthampton.

Naturally, I *was* honored, and I'd blush if I could. Of course, I accepted for the doglike reason that I never say no to anything; a policy that has never led me astray (not that there's anything wrong with that) and resulted in many fine adventures and more than a few doggie treats.

I was especially happy to learn that the art show was a benefit for Dakin, so that by going I could kill two birds with one stone (not that I would ever do that; killing birds is more of a cat thing) I could bask in praise (not that I care. OK, a little. I love it) all for a good cause and liven up a Saturday night which is often spent lying around the house waiting for my masters to come home from an engagement to which I am often uninvited.

But not this night. An event devoted to animal welfare was hardly about to claim dogs need not apply, and I must say that my arrival frankly dressed up the place. The artist greeted me warmly and escorted me to my portrait amid a chorus of oohs and ahhas, and photographs generally accorded to a visiting dognatary

It seems that Pat had come to admire my philosophy (I didn't know I had one) and that she had set out to capture the essence of my personality (dogonality, really) and that the result had been an 8 by 10 piece of oil on canvas, named simply but aptly, "Theo."

"I had always loved dogs and had them for many years," she explained. "I loved reading about Theo and really liked his outlook on life. And I really loved the work Dakin does, so it seemed natural to paint him and offer the painting as a fund-raiser."

She said she was a retired teacher and has been painting for about 15 years, always working from photos which she mounts in her studio for inspiration. Over the years, she had painted landscapes and still-lifes and an occasional portrait including mine, which took about eight hours to complete.

Of course I'm not exactly the king of England and paintings of me are few, but I can say without equivocation that it is the best portrait of me that I have ever seen.

All in all, it was a grand evening. I made some new friends, visited with a few acquaintances from Dakin, chowed down on dog treats and posed somewhat cooperatively for pictures along with the the artist. I learned from organizer Steve Del'acqua that last year the event raised a little over $500 and this year's goal was to top $2,000. I'm sure they will be glad to take donations at any time at http://www.dpvhs.org/support/, or by snail mail (not that there's anything wrong with snails) at Box 6307, Springfield Ma., 01101.

I nudged my master into giving a small donation (I had left my wallet at home) and after a bit more visiting as befitted my status of dog of the hour (aren't all dogs) was on my way and back home in time for dinner.

I spent the rest of the evening curled up awaiting the reviews which were uniformly kind and greeted with the modesty befitting someone who doesn't own a mirror. I hope that some art lover buys my portrait and that Dakin raises a ton of money from the citywide benefit, which I am sure will be used to help animals throughout the region.

And to Pat Coon I say that if a picture can say a thousand words, I'll be glad to settle for two.

Thank you.

POKER

Alert readers may recall that I attended my first art opening recently in Easthampton for the unveiling of my portrait as part of a fund-raiser for the local humane society.

Although I at first had some misgivings (I had nothing to wear, and inviting me anywhere where decorum is expected is always a bit dicey) I must say I had a fine time being the center of attention (what dog wouldn't?)

And while I of course loved the painting (after all, c'est moi) I hardly considered myself an expert much less an art critic, a job for which dogs are notoriously poorly qualified as we love everything.

Nevertheless, my modest foray into the art world apparently made me an authority on canine art (I assume the fraternity of canine art critics is small) and sparked a number of inquiries regarding my opinion on what many consider the highest form of dog art, specifically "Dogs Playing Poker."

For the uninitiated (which included me) a brief walk (I love walks, even metaphorical ones) through the Internet revealed that a " Friend in Need" referred collectively to a series of sixteen oil paintings by C. M. Coolidge, commissioned in 1903 by Brown & Bigelow to advertise cigars.

All the paintings in the series featured anthropomorphized dogs, (a fancy name for dogs pretending to be people, although what self-respecting dog would ever want to do that?) But the nine most famous works showed dogs seated around a card table where they have taken up residence in rec rooms, basements and college dorms ever since.

Coolidge never achieved much recognition in his lifetime but later, the most famous originals fetched more than $500,000 at auction and paid homage to famous painters Caravaggio, Georges de La Tour, and Paul Cézanne (see, I've only been an critic for five minutes and I'm already name dropping.) Despite (or maybe because of) the commercial success, most established critics have sniffed their nose (not that there's anything wrong with that) at the many reproductions of Dogs Playing Poker as "indelibly burned into ... the American collective-schlock subconscious."

Indeed.

Now I don't really know what schlock subconscious is, but it hardly sounds like a compliment. Frankly I rather liked the paintings as they seem to show dogs having a good time, although I can't imagine how.

After all, with the exception of a few border collies I know we're not good at sitting, and I suspect that if seven dogs were to sit around a poker table, the table would not be standing very long. Expecting dogs to hold onto cards bumps into the whole opposable thumb thing and there is no doubt in my mind that any accurate representation of such a scene would have the cards in little pieces halfway down the dogs' throats.

All of which begs (not that there's anything wrong with that) the bigger question of the limited interest that dogs of my acquaintance have with poker (my great finesse makes me more of a bridge man.)

Poker, as I understand it seems to rely on deception, a quality in short supply among dogs who wear their feelings on their sleeves (if they had any — sleeves that is — we have feelings in spades.) Despite the human adage that a dog's bark is worse than his bite, we rarely bluff and we have no use for money which seems to be the driving force behind most poker games. The only stakes we would be interested in playing for would be dog treats, which are readily available to us through our considerable charm.

No concealed aces needed.

So all in all, when it comes to "Dogs Playing Poker," or any of the other iconic Coolidge paintings, I must say that I just don't get it.

But maybe that's the way of art. It's all in the eye of the beholder.

So by all means feel free to decorate your house with just about any canine art you want.

Just don't count on inviting a bunch of dogs over and expect them to quietly spend the evening playing poker.

POLICE DOG

Big city police departments have come under a lot of fire lately but I am proud to say that none of it has been aimed at police dogs, many of whom I view as dear friends.

This is not that much of a trick since: 1) I am a friend of everything , even squirrels who clearly want no part of me, and 2) I think police dogs are - and there is no other way to say it - the cat's pajamas (even though I have yet to see a cat so decked out and can't even imagine what one would look like or why any feline of my acquaintance would be so inclined.)

In another life (which I am quite hopeful of since the present one seems curiously short), I hope to come back as a police dog and would have tried out for the job already if the application process hadn't been so lengthy and the training so rigorous.

I believe I have the talent if not the exact personality for the position. I love to chase after things and don't mind getting myself dirty on the job (in fact, I never met a puddle I didn't like) I work for scraps (yum) and while I never have (or would) bite a lawfully acting person, when I sink my teeth into a rawhide bone or a stuffed toy I don't let go unless commanded to do so and even then with some reluctance.

The only drawback I see is the general suspicion toward humans seem-ingly required for the job, but I believe with the right training, I could get over it. And even if I didn't exactly agree with a law (don't get me started on having to wear a leash in the woods) I certainly have the utmost respect for the canines in blue (although my favorite color is, of course, golden.)

Which is why I was glad to hear that the canine corps was getting its just desserts (I just love just desserts) recently when they participated in "Paws for a Cause," an aptly named fundraiser designed to raise winter clothing for the homeless by offering a chance to meet the Springfield canine corps and

offering an opportunity to actually hang one's head outside a police cruiser (which I agree has more allure to dogs than to humans, but whose problem is that?)

So it was on a sunny afternoon recently that I arrived at the Eastfield Mall in Springfield with mittens in hand (actually they were in my master's hand; I tend to eat them -- the mittens not the hand) and get my mug shot taken, which I had been assured was suitable for framing (not that police or police dogs would ever frame anyone.)

In addition to meeting several other wide-eyed dogs (we're always wide eyed even when not in the presence of dog celebrities) I jumped into the police cruiser and stood still (OK, I fidgeted) while the cell phones clicked away. And I would have stayed longer if I hadn't spotted what looked like a suspicious squirrel in a nearby tree prompting me to attempt a quick exit out of the cruiser's window.

The unauthorized attempted escape from a police cruiser turned out to be rather bad form for a would-be police dog and to all concerned looked more like criminal behavior so I can't honestly say that my high spirits actually advanced any chance of achieving cadet status. I gathered I would have to pursue my enforcement career as something of a lone wolf (not that there's anything wrong with wolves), and more like a bat-dog (ditto nothing wrong with bats) who would wait patiently on the front porch to be summoned by spotlight whenever the need for law enforcement might arise.

I expect it may be a long wait. Police dogs seem to have the crime scene around here pretty much under control and I'm not looking for the bat-dog signal to light up the sky any time soon. But should the police call, let me say that I am ready especially if there happens to be a sudden crime wave of acorns disappearing from the city's trees.

And while it may take a while (like forever) to actually apprehend a suspect it wouldn't be for lack of trying. And I know just where to begin the search.

FASHION

I have never thought of myself as fashion forward, but it turns out that after a fashion, I am.

Now most of the time, the fashion world and the dog world seldom meet. After all, we have little use for makeup, or eyeliner, and even less use for clothes as the maker of all things has made us quite happy in the skin we're in. With the exception of a few Hollywood dogs, most of us think clothing is just silly and what passes for French design, is mostly poodle stuff.

Of course we agree that good taste is timeless, but we think that applies a lot more to what falls off the table than what comes off the rack.

The closest I come to a fashion statement (other than "it's ridiculous") is the small wardrobe of bandanas I have amassed to mark holidays. If I must say so myself, I've always thought I cut a dashing figure greeting pint-sized ghosts and goblins in my tricked out candy corn bandana who come to the door seeking treats (frankly, I've always thought a nice lick on the hand makes a perfect treat.) By Thanksgiving, I trade candy corn for my turkey bandana (a better trade than the turkeys get) and then it's on to candy canes and snowflakes straight through the New Year.

So in that small way I am up to my neck in fashion, but I've always had the good sense to stop there. Until I heard from the good folks at the Dakin Pioneer Valley Humane Society who asked if I might consider joining my master in a walk down the runway as part of the charity fund-raiser fashion show on Feb. 28 at the MassMutual Center in Springfield.

Who me? Aw shucks. I really couldn't. Well maybe. OK, sure. But of course I hadn't a thing to wear, which turns out to be no problem since I really won't be wearing any clothes at all, (I'm still negotiating for the bandana) but will simply be the celebrity arm candy for my master who will be riding on my coattails (as if I had any.)

If I could laugh, I'd be in stitches (what's so funny about stitches anyway) at the prospect of my master being celebrated for his fashion prowess, which as far as I can see consists of remembering to put on his pants and somehow choosing from a closet full of Hawaiian shirts that no Hawaiian would be caught dead in.

In fact, the most common question I hear from my master's wife when he is preparing to leave the house is not "where are you going?" but "where are you going, wearing that?" leaving me to presume that unless the answer is to a clown convention he isn't going anywhere soon.

But of course, that is not my problem and the organizers of the fashion show assure me that with the entire resources of high-fashion sponsors at their disposal they are sure to come up with something for my master to wear that will send a chorus of oohs and ahhs, wafting down the runway along with a barrel full of donations to a very worthy cause.

Which of course is great for Dakin, a tribute to the sponsors, and a downright miracle for my master. But the truth is that a lifetime of experience has shown me that whenever the two of us go walking and someone says "ohmygod he's gorgeous," that whatever he's wearing, they are always talking about me.

CLINTON

I am not much of a celebrity watcher since to my way of thinking I AM the celebrity but I have to admit I was a tad star-struck during a recent late summer getaway to a certain island 30 miles out to sea where celebrities seem to grow like weeds (not that there's anything wrong with weeds.)

I met Bill Clinton.

And while it's just as true to say that he met me I must say that only one of us drooled just a tiny bit (not that there's anything wrong with that). There I was making my way down the cobblestoned main street marveling at the willingness of humans to part with $8 for an ice cream cone when I spotted the former president and his small entourage trying not to draw too much attention (why would anyone want to do that?) when we more or less just ran into each other.

Not having much experience with meeting ex-heads of state (do I curtsy?) I simply offered my usual glad-to-meet-you greeting and he in his former chief executive way quite democratically did the same. Meanwhile my mistress fumbled over the introductions, settling on calling him Mr. President (Bill seemed just a trifle chummy) and calling me, well me.

What followed must remain off the record in case I am ever invited to sit on the Supreme Court (and why not? My sitting skills are beyond reproach.)

Suffice it to say that we exchanged pleasantries (I am ever-pleasant) and he offered the standard judgment of princes and paupers that I seemed like a "good dog."

Upon hearing that I, like he, was a published author, he said that he had no doubt that I was a fine one and suggested that the current climate of catty discourse that passes for journalism these days might be considerably improved if the press corps contained a few more canine correspondents.

"Aw shucks," I wagged as if I heard such high praise from ex-presidents on a daily basis.

Our encounter after that was brief, as once you have been called a good dog by an ex-president there is surprisingly little left to say. Of course if I had happened to meet Queen Elizabeth there might have been hope for knighthood (Sir Theo has a certain ring to it.) But as it was the Secret Service contingent was getting antsy (nothing wrong with ants) and we soon parted company -- he going back to whatever ex-presidents do which as far as I could see was walk down the street and wait to be noticed and me, well, the same.

All in all it was just another afternoon in Nantucket where the sun always shines until you head to the beach and the clouds move in.

Meanwhile I'll always have a souvenir memory of the day that I met a celebrity just past the ferry dock on a gray day at the Gray Lady.

And I'd like to think it was a special day for Bill too.

I AM WHO I AM

RETRIEVER

Alert readers of this column may have noticed my amazement at the recent appearance of a traveling troupe of trained canines offering a dog thrill show (aren't we thrilling enough) in which the thrill comes from humans sitting quietly in seats while the dogs perform tricks such as Frisbee catching, tight wire balancing and feats of "magic" by which I imagine they mean pulling a rabbit out of a hat, although what dog, or rabbit for that matter would want that?

All of which begs (not that there is anything wrong with begging) the question of just what "tricks" are in my humble repertoire.

Let me at first say that the "trick" of being a dog and the one humans should most take note of is being ever cheerful, loyal, (mostly) obedient and the first to announce "count me in," for just about any fun activity that is on the horizon. And the less said the better regarding what are commonly thought of as dog tricks such as rolling over (pointless); chasing one's tail (ridiculous); or playing dead (just plain gross.)

Still, in the interests of full canine disclosure there is one trick particular to my breed which I feel compelled to admit that I am woefully deficient:

I am a lousy (not that there is anything wrong with louses, although they can be itchy) retriever.

There, I've said it. And I must say that I would be embarrassed if such a thing were possible for a dog (you should see the things I have put in my mouth with a straight face.)

In my defense, I can say only that the bar seems elevated for golden retrievers in the retrieving department. Portuguese water dogs are seldom asked to carry water, much less swim to Portugal. German shepherds can live quite well without shepherding and Irish setters are rarely asked to set. And yet a golden retriever who can't retrieve is in some way considered a traitor to his breed.

Nor is it that I totally lack the concept of retrieval. I love chasing after squirrels and chipmunks and am passingly successful at tracking down balls, socks, and sticks. The problem seems to be that I often lose interest in returning them to whence they came, or simply forget altogether that there is anything in my mouth (I would probably lose my tongue if it weren't attached) in which case it is technically my master who is the retriever while I am off pursuing whatever has next caught my admittedly fleeting attention.

But perhaps none of my retrieving deficiencies are as abject as my utter failure to do what my 1950s ancestors could seemingly do with ease:

Retrieve a newspaper.

If the stuff of situation comedies and black and white movies could be believed, newspaper retrieval along with fetching slippers (who wears those, and why the name if they are designed to prevent slippage?) is the sine qua non of 1950s dogdom.

Despite the seeming requirement of the idyllic dog leading the idyllic life in the "Leave it to Beaver" household (not that there's anything wrong with beavers,) I just never got the hang of it or even the point of newspaper retrieval.

Why not just check your phone?

Not that I can't see the use of newspapers for those folk brought up with the idea of checking your phone only when it rings. And I can see the obvious convenience of newspapers for taking into the bathroom (if I used a bathroom) or hiding behind when the topic of chores arises (if I were ever assigned chores) or clipping articles (especially mine) and hanging them on the refrigerator.

It's just that in general no matter how interesting, I'd pretty much rather chew on newspaper articles than chew over them. And judging from the chewed up socks, underwear, and tiny woodland animals I on occasion present to my owner, I suspect that -- 1950s folklore aside -- a chewed up newspaper is rather low on his list of preferred reading materials.

Now that I am approaching middle age, I suspect that the window of opportunity to acquire this particular skill set has closed (the old dog/new tricks piece of folk wisdom is true – it's not that we can't learn new tricks, it's that we prefer not to.)

I figure that my breakfast will arrive pretty much on time regardless of whether I retrieve the morning paper for my master or not.

Besides, he needs the exercise.

WATCHDOG

Robbers, drug fiends, and general bad guys stop reading now, I have a confession to make.

I'm not much of a watch dog.

Of course, it's not exactly like I was bred for the job. Like all golden retrievers I am genetically disposed to be loyal, loving, charming and kind, not exactly the traits you are looking for when you want to give miscreants the impression that you will tear them limb from limb at their first false move. There's a very good reason that no one has ever made a World War II movie in which the Germans are hunting for escaped concentration camp prisoners using golden retrievers.

And then there's that attention span problem. It's not like I don't chase things. Put a squirrel anywhere in sight and I'm off as if he had just robbed Fort Knox. But usually about 10 or 20 strides into the hunt, I spot a chipmunk and by time I ask myself, squirrel or chipmunk?; chipmunk or squirrel?, one is safely in a tree and the other deep underground as it dawns on me that maybe chewing on a stick is what I wanted to do anyway.

Not to mention that neither chipmunks nor squirrels are actually bad – just unfortunate not to have been born dogs. Even if I could work myself up to chase after truly bad guys, I'd be completely disarmed when they wanted to pet me, (and who doesn't) and then where would we be? If it's common sense not to bite the hand that feeds you, it's nearly impossible to sink your teeth into one that pets you. And then when it turned out that they were actually trying to escape from me (or the police) my response would hardly be to hold them against their will.

I'd be too astonished.

So no, a watch dog's life is not for me and I am glad to leave such duties in the paws of more menacing breeds (sure, I know there are no mean dogs

just mean owners, but still.) Which is why I am constantly surprised when on occasion people are actually afraid of me.

Maybe it's my bark, which is not only worse than my bite, it's much better, indicating the general glad-to-meet-you attitude I take to all living things and hardly a warning to stay away or suffer the consequences. Or perhaps it's my persistence to win over anyone showing the least resistance to my charms by just nuzzling them until they give in. I actually once had a non-dog lover ask if I could be trained to stop wagging my tail as it made her nervous.

Now why would I want to do that?

I suppose that I could add a little value to the household if I trusted only my master; greeted all strangers with suspicion; and bared my teeth a lot more often.

But that kind of approach to life is essentially undoglike and hard to turn on and off. I'd rather take my chances following the golden (retriever) rule – treat others like they have a treat for you.

And for those humans who insist upon seeing other folk as out to do them harm, I'd suggest getting a dog -- *and* a home security system.

WAIT... I HATE WAITING

Considering my rather fuzzy relationship to time (after all, it's only a construct even Einstein knew that) you might think that I'd have no trouble waiting.

And yet you'd be wrong.

I hate waiting.

It's not that I wasn't taught to wait. Waiting is right up there with sitting and staying in the dog obedience school catalogue of required courses. And a dog could make a pretty good living of treats by simply giving in every time the instructor said "wait."

But that's school, and any student knows that out in the real world there are more important things than listening to your instructors and none of them include waiting for anything.

It's not that I don't have patience.

For reasons that elude me, my master often leaves for hours on end (I'm guessing here, I really have no idea what an hour is) with his often cited but annoyingly nebulous reassurance that he will be back "soon," whatever that means. And generally I am content to entertain myself looking for low-lying scraps of food left on the kitchen table or pulling the stuffing out of my toys followed by going from room to room searching for a nice place to sleep until I realize that every place is a nice place to sleep.

Now I realize that to the undoglike mind this may sound like waiting but it is really just the canine version of twiddling my thumbs (if I had thumbs and had any idea what a twiddle was) because the minute I catch the scent of my master's return I forget sleep and food and dog toys and start jumping around as if the house were on fire.

Any sense of subtlety is immediately out the door, which is precisely where I want to be as I hand him first a sock, then a ball, while nuzzling him toward my leash and following all that with some underwear fresh from the laundry basket as a chaser (not that there's anything wrong with chasing) until he gets the picture that indoors is just not an option. (He's a slow learner; perhaps he should take a refresher course in owner obedience school.)

Meanwhile, I am totally (and appropriately) ignoring his commands to "wait," even when he predictably doubles down on this failed strategy by saying "wait, wait," as if the trouble here was with my hearing.

Which is yet another thing they should teach in owner obedience school: If I didn't listen to a command the first time, saying it the second time will only annoy both of us.

The fact is that being told to wait goes against my nature (and a dog's nature is pretty much all he's got) which tells me to go full steam ahead into whatever adventure lies ahead. A command to wait under these circumstances is like telling a racehorse in the clubhouse turn to "whoa."

Whatever for?

There's a world of parks, and woods and sticks and squirrels and mailmen carrying biscuits and fellow canines who smell just fine out there and I won't meet a single one of them staying in my house and waiting.

And while my master can at times be dumb as an ox (an unfounded slur, actually oxen can be quite clever), he needn't worry.

I'll lead the way.

FRIENDLY

Dogs don't generally give a lot of thought to the unanswerable questions that are woven into the fabric of our daily lives.

We seldom ponder the intricacies of the space-time continuum when our masters off-handedly say they will be returning "soon." We simply wait. We don't lose sleep (in fact sleeping is our basic default position) wondering why our life span is absurdly short or why evolution has chosen to favor those with two legs who in most cases aren't able to last an hour in the woods without checking their location on their cell phones.

Few of us wonder why are we so often referred to as "good dogs" but seldom great ones? What are cats really thinking? Why are there ticks?

I could go on but the answer to all these questions elicits a big yawn (hence our default position) from most canines who prefer to concentrate on the really pressing matters of the day such as is it time for a walk, and where's dinner.

And so it stands to reason that just about no dog would spend even a few minutes of his absurdly short life (not that I'm bitter about that one) wondering why are we so friendly? Yet human researchers have spent years of their absurdly long lives (there I go again) pondering just such a question and have now come up with a rather unsettling conclusion.

It appears that we are genetically defective.

Now you would not think that being a friend to all, loyal to a fault and greeting our masters as if they have returned from the 100-years war when they have in fact gone to the store for a quart of milk could ever be considered a defect. But a group of scientists from Princeton University (whose mascot is suspiciously a tiger) have announced that after years of dogged research the discovery that two defective genes associated with a rare syndrome in which humans show excessively friendly behavior are also found in dogs.

In short, all our tail wagging, face licking, and lap jumping cannot be attributed to our general devil-may care-friend-to-all-it-will-all-work-out, que sera que sera outlook that I always thought made us superior to the often dourness of humanity, but in fact is uncontrollable behavior linked to some rather frayed wiring along our GTF2IRD1 gene

It's enough to ruin my day, which apparently it can't because my master is due back any minute from the store and I am genetically required to hail him as a conquering hero even when along with the milk he brings such disquieting news from the chromosome front.

The upside for humans I suppose is that researchers can now take what they know about this particular genetic defect and perhaps help humans afflicted by the rare syndrome so they can become less friendly and hence more socially acceptable, at least to other humans.

I suspect that dog scientists will be less celebratory.

Friendliness suits us. It's much of what make good dogs great and any attempt to repair our defective genes would likely herald a future that is decidedly wolfish. Fixing a gene to remove our "excessive friendliness (whatever that is) might be called a great step forward for man but it sounds like a giant leap backward for dog-kind.

GOOD DOG

If there's one thing dogs know it's that knowing something isn't everything.

Oh we know the important things like when it's dinner time or time for a walk, or when our master's car is coming up the street even when he's still blocks away so we can prepare our just-got-back-from-the war daily greeting.

But there's an awful lot we don't know and we're OK with that. Subtract all the things we think we know that turn out to be flatly false; and the things that might be true right now but won't be true in the future, and the things that are going to happen anyway that we just can't do anything about (which is most things) and what you've got left is a big ball of worry.

And one of the big things that makes us different (OK, better) than humans is that we don't worry. No sir, no how. In fact, if dogs had a motto, it would be the calypso "Don't worry, be happy," sung with the full knowledge that it's not really a choice but a consequence.

When you don't worry; you ARE happy.

It's not exactly that we're against science so much as that we've transcended it. For example most of us can accept with mild detachment the scientific evidence that we're descended from wolves (not that there's anything wrong with wolves.) But that doesn't mean we're about to ditch our loving masters and predictable meal time to all of sudden starting running in packs.

That was then, and this is now – whatever then and now mean.

And those of us who are more faith based (we know better than to enter the whole religion/science debate) can note religiously that when the creator of all things gave Adam and Eve the order not to eat from the tree of knowledge he didn't give the same order to dogs.

We knew better.

All of which is a rather roundabout (not that there's anything wrong with roundabout) way of reporting some recent "scientific" research (we're not too sure what quotation marks mean, but it looks authoritative, or maybe sarcastic) stating that only 7.6 percent of dogs liked being hugged, with a little more than 10 percent having no opinion (the default choice for canines, I should think) and a whopping 81.6 percent showing significant signs of dog stress (whatever that means, but it doesn't sound good.)

Not like hugs? Bah humbug (not that there's anything wrong with bugs, except maybe ticks.)

I think I can speak for the 100 percent of the 7.6 percent dogs (even though I have never met a .6 percent dog -- must be a mixed breed) when I say that I never met a hug I didn't like. Oh sure, little kids can be a handful (ask their parents) and teens can be a bit rough (ask their parole officers) but I must say that speaking unscientifically (the best way) and with a sample size of one that being hugged ranks far ahead of most visits to the vet, the kennel, the ubiquitous "we'll be back soon" and any scientific experiment I can think of which just about always includes some kind of uncomfortable restraint.

So in conclusion (as scientists like to say) hug me, pet me, pat me, scratch me just above the forehead, or gently fold back my ears; just don't leave me alone. I guarantee you will get 100 percent of my 7.6 percent reaction 100 percent of the time.

And even the worst kind of hug beats by a country mile (not that there's anything wrong with country miles) the alternative of being ignored which in my highly unscientific opinion is far from desirable and quite frankly incomprehensible.

Unless, that is, you're a cat.

BAD DOG

Sometimes people think that just because I'm the only known regularly appearing dog columnist that I can do no wrong.

Ah, to wax poetic (which given our limited vocabulary is about as poetic as most dogs can wax), would that it were so.

The fact is that I'm no Lassie and while it's true that there's a good deal of Lady in me, there's also quite a bit of Tramp and for that I am largely unapologetic.

A dog's gotta do what a dog's gotta do. Or to put it another way I may be a good dog (I hear it often enough); I may on occasion be a great dog; but I'm not a perfect one.

Not that I'm bragging (is it bragging when you're recounting misdeeds?) but I've fallen off the good dog wagon more times than I care to remember.

There was the time when my master's brother arrived bearing freshly baked banana rum bread and left it on the edge of the kitchen table as he tempted dinner guests with the treat they had in store. Well, that's one dessert that never made it past the appetizers and it provided quite a main course for one whose table manners never included waiting to be served.

Yum.

Nor can I honestly say that it was a rare case. Danish, canolies, croissants, and at times an entire package of defrosting English muffins (frozen ones taste better than you might think) have known similar fates; left inadvertently and momentarily at dog-eye level and then suddenly to be gone as if taken by aliens for scientific testing.

Anyway, that's my story and I'm sticking to it.

About the only thing I can say in defense is that if humans were placed on a steady diet of kibbles and bits they too might take a more relaxed view of the occasional purloined pastry. I suppose such an argument might not

stand up in court but fortunately dogs are seldom prosecuted for such mis-
demeanors and I find that once I take a nibble off a plate, humans seem to
lose their appetite for it.

And I wish I could say that my misdeeds were only of the culinary variety. My puppy days were littered with chewed up socks, gnawed table legs
and feather pillows that were quickly de-feathered. In fact, there was a time
when the average life span of a newly purchased stuffed dog toy was less
than the average mayfly and my master once actually asked the pet store
if he could just cut to the chase by skipping the toy and just buying the
squeaky bladder inside, saving himself the cleanup.

Ah, to wax further poetic, those were the days, and I must say I thought
they were pretty much behind me until I happened to visit a dog acquaintance and there before me lay the cutest little stuffed toy with the cutest
sounding squeaker and cutest come-hither look I had ever seen.

I know, I should have resisted, and I did for all of about 30 seconds (which
to be fair, in dog time is more like four minutes) but the truth is that when
listing my attributes one can go through: kind, loyal, friendly and quite a few
others before reaching self-controlled.

And while my lawyer advised me to take the Fifth Amendment (I wonder
how that tastes) and that the evidence was circumstantial (one minute the
stuffed dog had its head, and the next it didn't) I had to admit that I was
pretty much caught dog-handed.

I suppose I could have rolled over a few times, jumped around the room,
frothed at the mouth and tried to plead insanity, but everyone knew better.
And if I had any money I would have gladly offered to make restitution but
a dog's resources are sparse so I tried the only defense that I know works
every time.

I just looked so darn cute.

I hung my head (humans like to see that, they think it means I'm
ashamed,) whimpered what could be construed as an apology and offered
some affectionate licks to the prosecutor as evidence that I had seen the
error of my ways.

I took the verdict of "bad dog" like a good dog, and promised that I
would henceforth be a model of canine respectability.

But the truth is who can really be sure when temptation calls?

Sometimes perfect dog isn't really on the table. Good dog will have to do.

MISTAKES

Everyone makes misteaks. Even, -- as you may have noticed – me; although in my defense I can say that a) I love steak and b) I'm a dog.

But even without the canine defense, I think I would have fared better than certain Chinese humans who it seems would not know a dog if it bit them (which I would never do) and who reportedly made the mistake (see I've spelled it correctly there; I learn from my misteaks) of buying a puppy on vacation believing it to be a Tibetan Mastiff and discovering that it was actually an Asiatic black bear.

Of course I make mistakes and some of them were whoppers. Like the time I mistook a neighborhood cat's come hither glance for a sign of friendship and was greeted by the full Monty of 10 claws, the remnants of which I carry just over my eyebrow to this day. Or the skunk I approached on one of my nighttime perambulations, curiously wondering what he was doing out so late, only to be given a mind-your-own business spray that took several baths and two days of exile to the back porch to recover from.

Still, I'd like to believe that if a dog – even a Chinese one – began chowing down on a box of fruit, and two buckets of noodles a day before ballooning to 250 pounds and walking around on its hind legs I might suspect that something decidedly undoglike was going on.

Apparently such confusion is becoming commonplace among the two-legged set as the case of the mistaken bear was followed in short order by a report of a woman who bought her "dog" from a Chinese pet store (I'm beginning to see a pattern here) only to learn that it was really a fox. In that case, (and I am not making any of this up) the fox owner told China's Shanxi Network Television that she paid close to $190 for the animal, believing the pet was a Japanese Spitz, a dog breed that looks similar to some foxes.

Well maybe to humans. I doubt that a dog, a fox, or even an Asiatic black bear would make such an error.

Nevertheless, the owner, whose horse sense (nothing wrong with horses) seems to have left the barn in the transaction, soon became suspicious when she noticed her new pet never barked (maybe it was just being polite) and became convinced she had been outfoxed when the pup refused to eat dog food for three months (a sure giveaway -- my record for declining dog food has never extended beyond a minute.)

Apparently this inability to recognize a wolf in sheep's clothing (a silly fable on so many levels -- sheep are dumb, but not that dumb; and no wolf would be caught dead in lambskin) is becoming widespread.

And although I never thought it would be necessary, I am offering a few humble tips to would-be pet owners so they might avoid purchasing the proverbial pig in a poke (whatever that means) and steer clear (nothing wrong with steers, if that is what you are shopping for) of the consequences of thinking they have bought a dog only to find out they are now the proud owners of, for example, a humpback whale. And so, my humble tips:

1) A dog wants to be where you are. Even if all you are doing is walking from the kitchen to the bathroom, a dog will consider the expedition as if you were leaving Spain in 1492 and about to discover the new world.

2) A dog's one and only guiding principle is "count me in." Want to go pick up dry cleaning – terrific. Weed the garden -- I can dig it; mail a letter (as if anyone does that anymore) -- deliver me.

3) A dog will greet you each and every day as if you are the most import-ant person in his world, which in fact, you are.

In short, if it looks like a duck, walks like a duck, and quacks like a duck it's probably a duck and not a dog, and most definitely not an Asiatic black bear.

And if one day you happen to be in a Chinese pet store and are about to buy a 250-pound alleged Tibetan Mastiff that is standing on its hind legs, skip the sales patter and just ask another dog.

One sniff and he'll know.

COIN

And so I report with some sorrow and a twinge of embarrassment the tale of a Jack Russell terrier named (appropriately if unimaginatively) Jack, who swallowed 111 pennies earlier this month and quickly became ill.

The 13-year-old pooch's owner rushed him to a Manhattan veterinarian where he (the dog, not the vet, and not the owner - I'm still getting the hang of English pronouns) was put under anesthesia and all 111 coins were removed. The zinc from the coins could be lethal (who knew? I'd expect a slight metallic taste, like a fine Greek wine - with a kick but harmless the next morning.)

Now told this way I admit Jack's bit of gastronomic experimentation sounds stupid, but it's what I call dog-stupid.

Yes, dogs do stupid things, such as chase after squirrels when there's no hope of catching one; and jumping into pond water in the middle of winter, but then again who doesn't? We don't go fishing on thin ice. We don't check smoldering coals on the barbecue by hand to see if they're hot enough. We don't get involved in land wars in Asia, and we never drink and drive.

So we are hardly alone in the stupid department, but we are especially dog-stupid about what we put into our mouth, which is just about everything. In our defense, this is largely because of our opposable thumb problem, which makes picking things up difficult (including a rifle, hence our success in staying out of wars), but which leaves us quite vulnerable to putting all sorts of silly things down our gullet.

Not to mention that our legitimate diet is rather restricted. We eat the same thing at the same time out of the same bowl and fancy silverware would be pretty much beside the point. So when we get a chance to check out something new, there's a good chance that sooner or later it will wind up between our teeth.

Personally, I favor socks and I'm seldom without one nearby even though I don't wear them (I'd much rather feel the earth beneath my feet.) I pluck them from the laundry basket; find them under the bed; and often as a household service just excavate them from the pile of clothes on the floor where my master has dropped them after a hard day's work. Socks are quite useful for chewing to relieve anxiety (a fact I'm surprised my master has yet to grasp) and I often wave them around to get attention should I need to go out or if dinner time is approaching. I've even buried a few in the yard as you can never tell when you might need a dirty sock on a rainy day.

Of course, socks aren't the only bits of clothing that have met the inside of my cheeks. I've been known to chew up gloves, scarves and the occasional piece of underwear (hardly my first choice for so many reasons.)

But I'm proud to say that I've never swallowed anything.

I may be dog-stupid, but I'm not THAT dog-stupid.

Which brings us back to Jack the Jack Terrier. I can happily report that the Manhattan veterinarian methodically removed all 111 coins from Jack's insides (I shudder to think of the method) and that he (Jack, not the vet) is fully recovered and back to what his owner called his normal self (whatever that is.)

I'd like to say that the experience has left Jack older but wiser, and he will never eat a penny again, but I'm not dog-stupid enough to ever predict what a dog will do.

Instead I'd suggest that Jack's owner keep his pennies in a piggy bank where they belong. And if Jack feels the need to chew on something, I'd suggest giving him a sock.

LEASH

I have a love-hate relationship with my leash.

Sure on the face of it, the leash is a sign of bondage. It cries out obeisance, servitude, and degradation. Looked at it in that way, it's practically slavery. And you can be sure that it's one of the first things we'll be getting rid of when we run the place.

The only time I've ever seen a person on a leash was when I spotted a mini-human of no more than 2 (that's 14 in dog years and hence all involved should have known better) harnessed to his rather bedraggled mom and paraded through of all things, a pet store (the irony may have been lost on the mom, whose sense of humor may have been suppressed by parenthood, which is odd, because it's the thing you need most.) Anyway, imagine my surprise to see a human child treated as if he were, well, a dog. What would come next, I wondered, a spiked collar? Branding? At the very least such treatment shows a certain lack of trust and is hardly a sign of civilization for a human and not much more so for a dog.

It's not really the indignity of being leashed I mind so much as the lack of freedom. Here I am investigating a particularly interesting leaf, or picking up the scent of subterranean vole, or hearing just the faint russell of a squirrel in a distant tree and it's pull, pull, in the opposite direction just because that's where my master wants to go. Now granted, he is the master, but I've always taken that to mean master of the house. Out in the woods, I like to think of us as equals (which is quite a concession as actually I'm quite superior, let him try leaping over tree trunks at irregular intervals at top speed; or getting out of a 20-foot ravine where there's no trail.) Still, I'll settle for equal, yet somehow a leash doesn't quite say that.

Face it, a leash says he's in charge and even if that's true in a technical way I don't like having my nose rubbed in it (not that I mind having my nose rubbed in most things, but indignity isn't one of them.)

So that's the hate part, you get it, even if you think being leashed is being done for my own good, which is something I find humans often say when they mean it's being done for their own convenience. But here comes the surprising part.

I love my leash.

Because at the other end of the leash is generally an adventure.

I'm never leashed around the house or while I'm napping, or watching television or doing any of the hundred things I do to kill time while my master is doing whatever he does when he leaves the house with the uncer-emonious command to stay and the ambiguous promise to be back soon. But the minute he returns and the leash comes out, I know I'm invited and I always have the same response.

Count me in.

As a matter of fact most of the time, all my master has to do is pick up the leash and I'm at the door ready to rock and roll. Whether the next stop, the park, or the woods, or a friend's house, I know one thing.

I'm out of here.

It's all practically Pavlovian, which many readers will recall as the condi-tioned response of humans to repetitive stimuli, first proven by Pavlov's dog more than a century ago when in an historic experiment having something to do with a bell became the first dog to condition his master to come home from a day at the laboratory and fill his dog dish BEFORE feeding himself for which he received many timely dinners while his master received only a Nobel prize.

But that's another story. The point is that I view my leash not so much as a sign of servitude, but as a magic carpet to adventure. No more stay at home, good dog while I have fun stuff. It's climb aboard big guy, adventure awaits.

It's not the sort of thing you have to ask me twice. So when the leash comes out, you can imagine how hard it is to say no.

And so I never do.

HAPPY

One of the main ways we're different (Ok, better) than humans is that for the most part we don't worry.

Oh sure we get a bit jumpy when we're on the way to the vet, and there's that kennel thing, which is mostly for show to make our owners feel guilty. But day for day we live pretty much day for day, which suits us fine.

Now admittedly there might have been some evolutionary advantages to thinking about the future for humans who in most other ways are pretty much sensory disadvantaged for living atop the food chain. I mean they can't smell worth beans, see in the dark, or run very well through a forest. And take away their opposable thumb and what do you have?

Prey.

But the price they pay for all that planning and striving, -- and face it, worrying -- about the future is that they don't handle the present very well.

You would never find dogs looking at next week's television schedule to see how they are going to entertain themselves over the weekend. They don't worry about missing anniversaries or birthdays or Valentine's Day, and April 15 doesn't strike fear into their hearts.

They don't lose a second's sleep thinking about their 401K or health insurance, or who is going to be elected president.

Because we learned a long time ago what only reggae singers seem to know.

Don't worry, be happy. Which by the way isn't two separate pieces of advice, but simple cause and effect.

Once you don't worry; you are happy.

I know what many of you are thinking – don't worry, be happy sounds pretty good in the summer when the sun is shining, but what about when winter comes?

And to me that sounds like you've been listening to too many working stiff ants and not enough grasshoppers. Tell me, if ants are so smart, why aren't grasshoppers extinct?

Because nature provides. Maybe not a BMW or a Nantucket summer home but come to think about it, I've been to Nantucket and seen plenty of dogs lolling around $12 million porches, and hanging their heads out of convertible BMWs. Because that's another thing dogs know.

What's better than a Nantucket home and a BMW?

An overachieving master with a Nantucket home and BMW, who needs a dog to keep him calm.

In other words, you can get pretty far with a wagging tale and winning smile if you're willing to rely on the kindness of strangers, which I admit doesn't always work so great for humans because they're worried that if they give something away they'll have less.

But it works great for us, because we know the truth is really on the other side of the coin.

When you give things away you have more.

Happiness, that is, not stuff.

Which is just another way we're different (and now you know why I mean better) than humans.

COUCH

My master says he can recall perfectly the plush red velvet sofa in the center of his grandmother's living room.

He never sat on it.

In fact, as far as he knew no one ever did. Instead along with the rest of the living room furniture, the sofa just stood there (can a sofa stand?) covered in thick plastic waiting for more worthy guests while all visitors were shuttled into the kitchen where apparently the real living took place.

Now dogs seldom cry but I must say that's the second saddest story I've ever heard. It's like giving a dog a bone and telling him he can't play with it. Who exactly was grandma and the red velvet sofa waiting for? The queen of England? Franklin Roosevelt? The messiah?

No one will ever know as the red sofa along with its plastic covered brethren were loaded into the Salvation Army truck on the day after her passing and presumably taken to furniture heaven where it waits to this day in full plasticized glory for someone, anyone to sit on it.

And while I have made up that last part, if true, THAT is the saddest story I've ever heard.

Fortunately, there is no danger of such a fossilized fate for the couch in my master's living room where I hold court regularly. When guests come calling I am glad to usher them into the living room where the family does some actual living and where they are welcome to sit any place they want to so long as it's not on the couch.

Of course such living room protocol took some training to establish. When I first arrived in the house I was politely told to STAY OFF THE COUCH (can you say that politely?) in a rampant piece of dogism that presumed the blue leather couch (I suspect it's really naugahyde -- naugas spare me your letters) was reserved for humans. It didn't take long for me to assert my counter claim by simply plopping myself on the couch and staying there, answering all objections with my charming doggy eyes and a fish-eye look (not that there's anything wrong with fish) toward anyone who might want to sit there.

Soon enough the humans were housebroken into the idea that the couch was mine and that they should arrange themselves around me to do such human things as watch television, munch hors d'oeuvres (I prefer to just grab them off the edge of the table) engage in spirited political conversation about how they would run the country if they were president and speculate pointlessly why the most comfortable seat in the house was occupied by a dog – as if that were a bad thing.

And that, as humans like to say, is that. By now the part of the couch that I call home is so scuffed up and doggy smelling (as if that were a bad thing) that guests give it a wide berth. Every so often, my mistress suggests getting some plastic to cover the couch but the subsequent and tear-filled retelling of grandma's red velvet sofa is enough to put the idea to rest. And I suppose there are plenty of products on the market that could make the couch smell less doggy but why would anyone want to do that?

So I guess that my status as official couch potato (not that there's anything wrong with potatoes) is assured. And should Franklin Roosevelt, the queen of England or the messiah ever show up they can just pull up a chair.

POOP

For the most part, dogs like to stay away from big issues. We'd much rather see the little picture. Despite what Freud's dog believed, for us a bone is pretty much a bone. Once you start seeing it as connected to other bones that are part of a skeleton that is part of a species that is part of genus that stretches back in time you pretty much miss the point which is to chew on it, or bury it.

Which is why you rarely hear of dog researchers or Nobel winners (although I haven't given up on the peace prize.) The price we pay for always fitting in, it appears that we don't care much where we fit in.

So imagine my surprise when I heard that the dog officer in Ipswich Mass. was on a crusade to spend $80,000 of taxpayer money to hire a company named PooPrints to create a DNA database of the town's 2,000 dogs so that stool samples could be matched against the database and fine those who violate the town's pooper scooper law.

Sounds very big picture-ish for what should be a matter of common sense and common decency which is that dog owners should pick up after their pets. What part of that, I wonder, do humans not understand?

Now I must admit it was not always like that. My master says there was a time in his childhood where just about no one picked up after his dog. That was pretty much the point of walking them outside and the philosophy (if you could call it that) was walker beware.

But of course that was before seat belts and bike helmets and no smoking ordinances and a boatload of other perfectly sensible ideas that had somehow escaped the notice of previous generations but which today hardly merit mentioning until you realize that someone has harnassed the power of modern science to create PooPrints and at least one person thinks that paying $80,000 for their services seems like a good idea.

And now at the risk of being indelicate, a word about poop. We agree, it smells, it's messy and it seems to be attracted to the soles of human shoes. But we didn't make the system, we've just stepped into it. It's all part of the big picture, the great chain, in which we are simply part of the pass-through. Despite what some owners think, "doing our business" (as if we were the wolves of Wall Street) is not exactly the high point of our day. If we could go for a walk just for the exercise, that would be fine with us (although I suspect there would be far less dog walking if that were the case.) And short of tasking scientists with giving us an opposable thumb to use the toilet (and who would want to open that can of worms – not that there's anything wrong with worms) I think we are pretty much stuck with the wisdom of Descarte's dog, "I poop therefore, I am."

And so big picture. Dogs poop, humans are in charge; get over it. Forget the dog DNA registry, PooPrints and the $80,000 which could buy a very nice dog park and still have enough left over for free poop bags for every responsible dog owner in town. Man up (or dog up, or whatever politically correct noun comes to mind) and accept that poop happens.

It's what the humans do about it that counts.

DOGGY BAG

Dogs aren't very good at making economic predictions as we have no concept of money and even less notion of the future. Asking a dog whether a bird in the hand is better than two in the bush would require us to know what kind of bird, what kind of bush, what was a bird doing in a bush and by the way what was the question again?

So I'm not surprised that dogs weren't asked to weigh in on such questions as would a tax cut now be worth a possible budget deficit later, but if I were, I would remind humans to consider the fate of the humble doggy bag.

There was a time when doggy bags were well, for dogs and frankly we never knew how good we had it. Our masters would depart for a night on the town with the traditional vague promise to be back "soon," and upon their return would bring back the remnants of the evening's repast for us.

And we were grateful for it as we never look a gift horse in the mouth (a particularly human idiom – dogs know it's rude and it annoys the horse.)

After all, we knew full well that we had done nothing beyond our usual lovableness to deserve such a treat and were seemingly being rewarded for doing what we always do when our masters leave, which is largely to wait around for their return.

In short, the entire doggy bag concept seemed like a refund of a bill never paid (not that we ever paid bills) and we came to accept it much as we would a welcome pat on the head just for being, well us.

Until without notice the doggy bag with the added insult of a mixed metaphor, flew the coop; passing us right by and landing in the refrigerator, the contents of which showed up on our master's plates at ensuing mealtimes with nary a crumb for us and forcing us to beg (not that there's anything wrong with that) for something that we had always considered rightfully ours.

Sure no one had exactly promised us that the doggy bag would be for dogs, but with such a name what doubt could there be about its intended recipient? I mean you wouldn't expect a dog house to house elephants; or feed a dog biscuit to a fish.

And yet without a word from us we were cut out of the doggy bag business and what had seemed to us a natural consequence of trickle-down economics (our masters eat higher off the hog, and we get the hog leftovers – not that there's anything wrong with hogs, or leftovers) became just another way to load the plate of those who had a pretty good seat at the table to begin with.

Now I'm not saying that that's what will happen to all the benefits that humans are waiting to gobble up from the promised tax cutting fever that has gotten hold of Washington. But before they start counting their chickens before they're hatched (something chickens would never do) they might do well to remember the tale of the doggy bag (not that there's anything wrong with tails, many of my best friends have them).

Sometimes you think you're getting leftovers; but you're really just left holding the bag.

EAT

Considering that I eat the same meal every day, you might think I'm not much of a restaurant critic. Most of the things restaurants consider delicacies, I consider colleagues (frogs are a bit jumpy for my taste, but it would be hardly polite to consider eating their legs over it.)

Still, I do have my opinions (although few humans ask) and if pressed, my restaurant reviews would follow a simple rule. No stars for eateries that stop us at the door, and four stars (I would go higher but my counting skills get weak once I get off one paw) for those that pull up a water dish when we arrive.

And I am glad to say that history seems to be on my side as more and more establishments are putting out the welcome mat at restaurants, retail establishments and big box stores (I've always loved big boxes) recognizing that not only is it the non-dogist thing to do, it's actually good for business.

Careful readers may recall that it was my getting the boot (not that there's anything wrong with boots) from a local coffee shop (OK, it was Starbucks) that launched my career several years ago as the nation's only regularly appearing canine columnist. My feeling then as it is now, is that dogs are no better or worse behaved than human clients and -- with the exception of young children who bring behavior problems of their own to the table -- quite a bit more charming.

And while some would argue that not everyone loves dogs, I would say pity on them, I would be willing to chalk up their rather limited opinion of proper dining companions to some obvious trauma from their childhood (they always wanted a dog for Christmas, but due to an obvious mix up in communication with Santa just kept getting presents instead.)

As to the base charge that we smell, I should point out that with olfactory nerves 25 times more sensitive than humans, malodorous restaurants (and

their customers) are far more a problem for us than for humans, who would certainly abandon their objections to us if only they could smell what we do.

And so I applaud (if I could) the growing number of restaurants that now consider themselves "dog friendly" (although I am a bit unclear as to when doing the right thing became friendly) and I am happy to accompany my human companion into such establishments where I make sure to be on my best behavior.

This often means taking my usual position on the floor and curling up under his chair while ignoring the crying infants; sullen cell-phone toting teens; and squabbling couples who are actually taking up seats and who feel it is perfectly OK to share their personal dramas with paying customers who have come out to eat specifically to avoid such bickering at home.

I am ever kind to the staff, never asking them to put the dressing on the side (why bother); more rolls (although I'd love some); care about my food allergies (I have none) or blaming them when the food arrives cold (my food is always cold.) I never overdrink, inappropriately flirt with waitresses in front of my wife, or send a meal back (no dog in history ever has.) And on the not so few occasions when passersby stop at my table to say how beautiful I am, I accept the compliment with a jaunty wave of my head and wish them bon appetite.

In short, and if I do have to say so myself, I am the perfect dining companion, as are all the canines of my acquaintance; so much so that I predict there may come a day when some ahead-of-his-time entrepreneur comes up with the idea of opening eating establishments with a menu aimed specifically at us.

And you can bet we wouldn't think of barring humans to our tables. They'd be perfectly welcome as long as they sat quietly by our feet.

BEG

And now for a few kind words about begging.

I'm a beggar. There, I've said it. If admitting the problem is the first step to recovery, then I've made some progress in a twelve steps sort of way, I suppose.

But of course not to belabor the obvious, the twelve steps to recovery are for people, and I'm a dog. After seven steps, I'm just getting started on my way to chasing squirrels or romping through woods or tracking a scent. And if all that sounds like I'm begging the question of begging, let me say it once again, for the record:

I'm a beggar.

Not the kind of human beggar of course, who is most likely found around bus stations, and on street corners presenting the ethical dilemma of a fellow being seemingly in need who just might be playing you for a chump. You'll never find me with a sad tale of how I only need $10 more for a bus ticket to see my grandmother in New Hampshire; or spinning a story about how my car just ran out of gas and could you spare a fiver for a gallon, when what you suspect is that money will go directly into a gallon of cheap wine and it's back on the street with a hand out again.

First of all, dogs don't put their hands out. It throws off our balance. And we don't drink wine, finding the smell of fresh grass is quite intoxicating enough. We barely knew our grandmothers and have only the vaguest idea of what a New (or old) Hampshire is. Our needs are simple. A piece of cheese, a leftover hot dog, perhaps a cheese doodle.

Who could deny us that?

Apparently, plenty, judging from the rather large number of humans who think dog begging is bad form and shows rather inelegant breeding. Perhaps they would like me to get job? Or grow my own food? Or apply for a research grant?

Give me a break. With the exception of show business, the number of ways for a dog to enter the cash economy are few. Sure, we could go native and hunt down our own food, but I doubt most of our masters would really want to live in that world, with us bringing back small rodents, goose eggs and who knows what from the wild to supplement our meager puppy chow and water rations.

And for those who think that we should somehow be above trying to charm our way into a piece of salami every so often, let them try eating the same thing every day from the same bowl and see how long it takes them to seek some variety.

Sure, begging makes some humans uncomfortable, but I beg to differ on the solution.

Wouldn't it be better to work out some compromise which retains our dignity yet rewards our charm? Isn't that why humans brought us home in the first place?

In my household, the only commandment is no begging at the table. This is understandable. I don't like to be bothered while I'm eating. Why should it be different for humans?

Before dinner is a different story, where I like to think of myself as a combination sous-chef/palace food tester sampling the evening fare as my master goes through its preparation; nodding my approval over a dollop of finely crafted creme fraiche or politely gagging my distaste for culinary experiments gone awry which, frankly, shouldn't be fed to a dog.

Clearly, anything that falls to the ground should be fair game as our notion of the 10-second rule is quite a bit more liberal than most humans. And apres dinner, we should be allowed first crack at the dishwasher where a thorough licking should be thought of as a prewash.

Now, was that so hard?

To recap, no begging at the table. Before and after that, think of my modest requests as an opportunity to do the right thing.

And one day, when dogs rule the world and humans are reduced to eating the same gruel night after night from ceramic dishes that haven't been washed for weeks, we'll look kindly on the occasional request for scraps.

After all, charity begins at home.

CHICK MAGNET

It's no secret among the single set that we canines are often referred to as "chick magnets."

I see it all the time. My master and I are walking down the street when a comely female human stops dead in her tracks and says right out loud, "You're so beautiful."

And they never mean him.

Naturally, I take such attention in the manner befitting a dog - I lap it up - playfully offering my nose for a rub, or allowing some good natured petting around my ears, after which I am content to go about my business. And you would think that would be the end of it, until I learned recently of an Internet dating site devoted exclusively to the idea that many humans seem incapable of knowing their own hearts and trading on my chick magnetism to help them find true love.

Called appropriately *mustlovepets.com,* the site immodestly calls itself "the premiere pet finder destination for meeting and/or dating quality animal lovers who are single and seeking a sincere relationship with other dog or cat lovers."

At *mustlovepets,* all animal lover profiles are pre-screened and qualified to - and I am not making this up - "ensure a safe and enjoyable dating relationship."

It's a good thing I can't talk, because if I could, I would be speechless.

I'm just a dog, of course, but no matter how many ways I parse that phrasing, I can't see how having a pet brings one any closer to a safe and enjoyable dating experience, unless, of course, you were planning to date a dog.

Not that that would necessarily be a bad idea considering some of the bachelor/bachelorette shows I've seen on TV where the contestants seem to

Photo by Dave Roback.

have no better idea of what they are looking for in a mate than your average sea turtle. And it's certainly true that dogs are fun loving, unflailingly loyal and extremely affectionate, all qualities that would make us wonderful dates - even if we come up a bit short in the conversation department.

But there seems to be no avoiding the elephant in the room that would apply equally to anyone considering dating an actual elephant.

We're not human.

Now perhaps you could argue that the qualities that would make one a good pet owner would naturally make one a good human being and hence an attractive date, but alas, that is not entirely true.

Many humans of my acquaintance are perfectly fine pet owners but have the social graces of a raccoon - they stay out all night, thrive on garbage and never back down from a fight.

Sure they can be trusted to put out food twice a day and walk us around the block, but is that really enough to hang a hope for a walk down the aisle and happily ever after?

The website goes on to promise that the friendly and competent staff is at your service seven days a week to accommodate all your dating needs even if it's just a "pet peeve."

Now putting aside the "pet peeve" swipe, just what dating "peeve" might a dog be responsible for? Slobbering? An unnatural affinity for chasing squirrels?

About the only part of the web site that I can see any use for is the invitation to post a picture of the pet along with the potential date to see if a match might be suitable.

That way, should a friend ask who you've been dating lately and you show the picture and she says "he's beautiful," you'll know exactly who she means.

GROOM

I don't like to brag (my limited speech makes me naturally modest) but I consider myself quite well-groomed.

Oh sure, there has been the occasional roll in the mud (don't knock it until you've tried it); the not exactly authorized leap into a weedy lake while chasing a Frisbee and a few close encounters with a neighborhood skunk but I chalk them up to a combination of canine exuberance (the mud); my good breeding as a retriever (the Frisbee) and my hail fellow-well met friendliness (wasted on the skunk).

In just about all cases a simple hosing down and a quick shake of the fur (the deskunking takes a tad longer) is usually enough for me to revert to my charming self and ready to greet my public and collect the usual accolade of "he's beautiful"

Just the way I am.

Which is why I am constantly surprised to find myself on special occasions (to me every occasion is special) loaded into the car and whisked off to "the groomers" the mere mention of the word to my limited vocabulary sounds like "doomers" and which elicits about the same end-of-the-world response.

Nor are my apocalyptic fears reduced to hear my master say that she will be back "soon," (always a problematic word) and leave me surrounded by all sorts of cutting, clipping, and shaving devices that would make the Marquis de Sade's dog slobber (nothing wrong with slobbering per se, but I would just as soon not have at it my expense).

Oh, it starts innocently enough with the doomer/groomer telling me I'm beautiful (how many bad endings have started with those words) and assuring my mistress that I will calm down just as soon as she leaves (fat chance).

And then the moment she inches out the door, out come the clippers.

To cut to the chase (nothing wrong with chases and believe me the narrative is hardly the only thing being cut here) the remaining hours are not a pretty sight. Everywhere I turn there are straps and harnesses designed to keep me still (the farthest thing from my mind) as I am prodded and pushed into all sorts of undignified positions in an effort to trim my nails, unknot my fur, brush my teeth, wash and blow dry me and generally reach into all sorts of unmentionable places in an effort to turn me into a calendar version of myself.

None of which is painful exactly (except to my pride) but hardly a walk in the park (and I know my walks in the park). Sure I am pronounced "beautiful" after all the fussing but isn't that pretty much where I started except now there seems to be a lot less of me to fawn over (nothing wrong with fawns, who generally live perfectly fine lives without coming near a groomer.)

Soon (but certainly not soon enough) my mistress returns and despite my initial feelings of betrayal I am overjoyed to see her (it's not my fault; I'm incapable of holding a grudge.) For all my travails I am awarded a snappy bandana and the accolades of the groomers who are doing some pretty good fawning of their own saying how much "fun" I had and what a perfect gentlemen I had been.

All lies of course but my limited vocabulary makes a spirited cross examination of their testimony problematic. Instead I make a beeline (nothing wrong with bees – no grooming for them either) for the door with all concerned remarking how well groomed I looked, never suspecting the "dirty" but delicious thoughts of mud puddles and weedy lakes dancing in my head.

SMELL

It's not exactly something we admit in polite human company, but get any two dogs together down and dirty and we'll readily concede.

We smell.

Not that there's anything wrong with that. Just as flowers smell like flowers, trees smell like trees, voles smell like voles (how else do you think we find them under a foot of fresh snow) and people smell like – well, people (and believe me, if you'll allow the mixed metaphor, it's not a pretty sight.)

You'd never see us in a commercial (and we've been known to appear in some pretty silly commercials) for dog deodorant or "natural" soaps because covering up the way we smell is the last thing any dog would want to do.

I mean why have a sense of smell that is the envy of the animal kingdom (and miles ahead of humans' puny olfactory abilities) and then befuddle it with a combination of chemicals that makes us smell like an Irish spring.

If we wanted to do that, we'd just find an Irish spring and splash around in it.

And although you don't often hear of products marketed as "romp in the leaves," or "skip through the mud", or "roll around in poop" I can proudly say I've done all of those and while it may make my master put his nose up (whatever that means) I've never heard a fellow canine complain.

Because while humans are constantly reminding us, we smell, the truth is we SMELL LIKE DOGS, which as you can tell from the excessive capitalization is exactly the way the creator of all things intended us to smell. Get a pack of us together and no one has to ask us where we've been. A few sniffs, and we know.

It all comes back to our greatest superpower – our all-knowing nose. Should Hollywood ever get around to producing "Bat-dog vs. Superdog" the climatic fight scene would never get much farther than when

Bat-dog (whatever that means) sniffs Superdog, whereupon they both discover they smell like dogs and just go home, an extremely agreeable conclusion, although one which hardly leaves much room for Bat-dog vs. Superdog part 2.

And yet for some reason humans just don't get it (although in their defense there are many things they don't get, such as why digging is so much fun, and how you can entertain yourself for days with an old sock). Without realizing what a compliment it is, they insist that after a few hours in the woods we smell "doggy," roll down the car windows (not that there's anything wrong with that) and upon our return home immediately set about hosing us, brushing us and threatening us with a trip to the groomers as if we had actually done something wrong.

Fortunately like many human intentions, these notions soon pass and we can go back to self-grooming which consists largely of self-sniffing and fondly remembering "oh, the places we've been." For as any dog can tell you, being swamped with soap, mouthwash and toothpaste, doesn't hold a candle (and why would anyone want to do that) to the joys of simply being swamped.

DESIGNER DOG

Except for Gregor Mendel's dog, and the unfortunate dog of Frankenstein, I'd say that most canines have little interest in genetics.

We don't really believe in messing with Mother Nature, and we're pretty content to deal with the genes we have. Golden retrievers for example are genetically predisposed to hip problems, but you don't see us cooped up in laboratories trying to manipulate our genes in search of the perfect joint. We'd much rather be out in the woods chasing squirrel DNA and smelling the roses, even if it means we'll be spending our senior years sleeping on the porch (not that there's anything wrong with that.)

Personally, I've kind of resigned myself to the fact that hip problems are the price I pay for my swagger.

Still I can't help picking my ears up (you think it's so easy, you try it) when humans announce that through meticulous research and careful gene manipulation they've come up with the perfect dog.

And here I thought that was me.

But apparently not, as that so-called honor goes to the "cava-poo-chon" a genetically enhanced mix of King Charles spaniel, bichon frise mix and miniature poodle which costs $2,000 and scientists claim is smart, healthy, hypoallergenic, practically barkless and likely to live to 20, which in dog years is well over 100.

It also happens to weigh between 10 and 15 pounds.

Now that may be some scientist's idea of the perfect dog, but I have to say it's nothing to jump up about (not that there's anything wrong with that.)

Without my bark how would I let my master know it was time to go out? How would I protect him from strangers? Who would tell him it's time for dinner (mine of course, he's on his own)?

And all this talk about intelligence strikes me as somewhat dumb.

Truthfully, how much smarter do I have to be? I fetch when I want to, sleep when I feel like it and, with the exception of never catching squirrels, have no regrets.

Humans don't really get it, but there comes a time when intelligence gets you into more trouble than it saves you from, which is pretty much why you can be sure you'll never hear of a dog trying to build a nuclear bomb.

Thinking leads to overthinking. I'd rather be romping.

Which leaves the longevity thing. Sure, theoretically I'd love to live a little longer than nature has in store. Heaven can wait, I always say, since life down here is pretty darn good. But if the price to be a canine centenarian is I'd have to spend my prime weighing 10 pounds, I'd have to say no thanks.

And while being cava-poochon size may be an advantage when traveling by plane, or fitting into a Manhattan apartment, I see no upside in the forest where just about no one will take your name seriously (trust me, poo boy) and where you are likely to meet all sorts of woodland creatures who could easily mistake you for a large vole.

Being genetically modified to live to 20 is not much of an advantage if you get devoured the first time you go outside.

So, all things considered I think I'll just pass on the whole designer dog thing. Messing around with Mother Nature is a tricky business (which is why you'll never see a dog blamed for global warming) and honestly I can't think of anything much better than being who I am. And judging from the high praise I get around town, lots of other folks seem to think that too.

So scientists can keep their genetically designed King-Charles-spaniel-bichon-frise-mix-miniature-poodle-cava-poo-chon.

I'd rather be me.

TECKNO

I have met the future, and his name is Teckno.

Teckno is a robot puppy and so you will not think I am making this up I will quote from his online ad which I suppose is the Internet answer to the childlike question, "how much is the puppy in the window?"

Teckno the Robotic Puppy is the robot puppy that acts just like a real pet puppy. Teckno walks forward, backward, right and left - His tail, ears and head move as well! Teckno expresses emotions through his color-changing eyes and puppy sounds - He barks and whines just like a real puppy. Teckno comes with a bone and a ball to play fetch - Teckno loves to chomp on his bone! Wireless Teckno Translator included! Translator also makes Teckno dance, speak, walk and more!

Deluxe version, $389.50. Soul not included.

That last sentence is mine. And not to get too metaphysical about it there is the metaphorical fly in the ointment (not that there's anything wrong with flies.) I have no doubt that all the claims the advertisement makes for Teckno are true.

His tail moves, I'm sure; but does it wag? He chews on bones but what does he taste? He expresses emotions with his eyes, but do those eyes jump when he sees you walk through the door at the end of the day? And can he really "love" his bone, or anything? He can fetch but is he fetching? Who knows? Perhaps he can even catch squirrels, but would he ever feel the joy of taking off after one?

I'm probably spitting into the wind here (Teckno can probably do that too) but is this really the future for man's best friend? Sure, you could maybe turn your friend into a robot and have him fetch, or cook, or engage in witty repartee, but would he still be your friend, or would he be a vacuum cleaner who just looks familiar?

The way I see it, Teckno, however advanced he becomes, can never become man's best friend, because he can't be a friend at all. And while he can "act like a real puppy," he can't be a real puppy any more than Pinnochio's dog could be a real dog, or a multi-national insurance company can be "just like a neighbor."

He can act like he loves you. But he can't love you.

Now maybe this is a fair trade for not howling in the middle of the night, and not waking up too early and nuzzling you out of bed to go for a walk. I'm sure Teckno can be less trouble and more convenient than a real dog, but who wants a dog for its convenience?

Let's put it this way. If I could trade in my master for a Teckno master that would feed me without being asked, walk me wherever I wanted, and put me in the front seat and his wife in the back, but couldn't for one moment know the joy that comes from a walk in the woods together just the two of us; would I do it?

Not on your life. But what do I know?

I'm only a real dog.

TECKNO REVISITED

Alert readers may recall that several years ago I stumbled (metaphorically of course, I am in fact quite sure-footed) across "Teckno" a robotic puppy whose animatronic claim to fame was that he "acts like a real puppy" (as if that's a good thing) with the single glaring exception that he is not a puppy at all but a carefully disguised collection of nuts and bolts that can bark, fetch, and chew on a bone without the minor (in my mind) inconvenience of feeding, walking and poop scooping that accompanies the boatload of love that comes with the real thing.

At the time this discovery sparked all kinds of epistemological questions in my living brain. His tail moves, I wondered. But does it wag? He chews, but does he taste? He fetches, but is he fetching? Like Hamlet's dog (a character curiously cut from the final script), I asked of the robot canine, "to be or not to be," and came up with the simple answer.

Not.

Which I thought would have settled the question, but what I hadn't counted on was the march of science that had taken on the challenge of improving a bad idea the result of which was the recent announcement by Toymaker Hasbro that after considerable success in marketing an animatronic cat (no surprise there; cats seldom ponder the meaning of life) they have now decided to enter the brave new world of creating, gasp, a robot golden retriever.

It was, as French poodles like to say, déjà vu all over again.

The companion pet, thankfully unnamed (I suggest Frankenstein) will bark in response to hearing his master's voice which in itself would be annoying enough (actually I hate barking and only do so when absolutely necessary.) But with the help of the National Science Foundation (don't they have anything better to do, like say cure cancer?) plans are under way to enable the new age robo-pooch to find lost objects, issue medication reminders and generally help around the house (will he do laundry?)

Not that I'm threatened. All right, a little. You bet.

"It's a lovely, non-medication intervention for people who are upset" gushed one of robo retriever's endorsers, obviously overlooking its upsetting effects on the living dogs of the house who confine their admittedly self-centered reminders to circling the supper dish and scratching at the front door.

There was no denying that in the three years that I had thought I had put the Teckno question to bed (nothing wrong with going to bed) the robotic dog had learned some new tricks. Nor did it help that the proposed enhanced mechanical dog would sell for quite a bit less than my current market value (not that I care about money, but humans seem to notice such things).

In short, the challenge of a mechanical arch-rival had me worried (something I'm sure robo-dog isn't programmed to do.) After all, my memory is admittedly dim (although I never forget dinner) and I don't do laundry. Might I be traded in someday for a pill-reminding, cell phone detecting, non-pooping version of myself?

But then I déjà-vued my own thoughts about Teckno all those many dog years ago.

A mechanical dog, I wisely said to myself at the time, can search for your keys and remind you of your pills until the cows come home (nothing wrong with homebody cows) but he'll never be any more a part of your household than your vacuum cleaner.

He can act like he loves you. But he can't really love you.

Truer words were never spoken.

Even if I had to say them myself.

Again.

Dog TV

DirectTV is making no bones about where it believes its programming is going.

To the dogs.

I am not making this up. The largest U.S. satellite television provider has begun airing DogTV, a $5.99-a-month premium channel designed - in marketing speak - "to comfort animals and stave off loneliness when pet owners are out of the house."

To keep dogs stimulated, DogTV promises "scenes with and without other animals, animation sequences and a variety of moving objects," the network said on its website. It also offers relaxation programming with soothing music. Programmers promise that the colors and audio are adjusted to fit a dog's senses, whatever that means.

I've never been much for TV, cable or otherwise, although my master has at times left the TV on when he is out of the house, largely to keep away burglars, which when you think about it is kind of insulting.

Aren't I enough?

And it's not like dogs are strangers to the entertainment industry. There's Lassie, of course, and Rin Tin Tin, both of whom were hard to warm up to. Too prissy; too military. I did spot a bit of myself in Lady and the Tramp (and I was no Lady) but 101 Dalmatians left me cold. I mean dalmatians are cute in a spotty kind of way, but 101 of them is extreme, and using them for coats is just sick.

Who knew that I was just another target audience waiting to be discovered by programmers who have apparently run out of love-starved bachelorettes, overweight losers, and ex-celebrities willing to dive off high boards just to make a splash.

Maybe it's because I'm a dog, but I must say I don't get it. Dogs have no disposable income (unless you count the fact that we've been known to eat pennies). Few of us qualify for credit cards and malls tend to sniff at us (and vice versa).

The closest we come to being shoppers is when we venture into pet shops and notice that the most breakable and edible objects are placed exactly at our level.

None of which makes us a target audience.

Most of the time, when our masters leave the house, we do the sensible thing and simply go to sleep. That way we're rested up for whatever adventure may come along next.

We're not against fun, not by a long shot. In fact, we live for it. But watching other dogs at play on a small screen strikes me as just sad.

I'd rather nap.

Gilad Neumann, chief executive officer of the dog channel, claims that dog parents are constantly seeking solutions to ease the loneliness and boredom of their stay-at-home pups.

Putting aside the obvious fact that my dog parent is, well, a dog, let me offer an even more obvious solution.

Play with us. Or take us to the park or put us in the back seat of the car and roll the window down, or try wrestling a bone out of our mouth.

But if you are intent upon leaving us, take the $5.99 a month you would have spent on Dog TV and buy us a brand new toy with a squeaky bladder in it.

Then when you come home, we can both watch TV while I chew on the bladder and you clean up the shreds.

BLESSED

I have been blessed, and don't I know it.

No one has to tell me that life has been kind to me. I could have been born a junkyard dog, shivering on the streets and living by my wits instead of by my charm. Or in some country where humans actually eat dogs (how sick is that? I don't even eat sushi.) Or maybe I could have not been born a dog at all. Maybe a vole, or a tick, or a raccoon in which case I'd have to go through life scared of myself.

The point is that there are a lot worse hands that life could have dealt me than two square meals a day (plus all I can beg); unconditional love from masters who jump when I bark; a nearby park for romping; and the ability to turn the heads of most humans I meet who pronounce without the least provocation that I'm beautiful.

Like I said, I've been blessed, but this week, I was officially blessed.

There I was at the Mercy Medical Center feeling like Irving Berlin's dog putting on my top hat; tyin' up my white tie; puttin in the shirt studs; and brushin' off my tails for the annual "Blessing of the Animals." Of course the top hat part was mostly metaphorical (hats don't stay on me very long and I could never see the point); same with shirt studs. But the polished nails I had, I'm always wearing my tail and I couldn't have looked spiffier as I waited patiently alongside a handful of other dogs, and cats for the welcoming words of Sister of Providence Madeleine Joy, of the center's spiritual care department.

"We bless these animals because of our love for them and to show them our unconditional love and we are especially aware of St. Francis on his feast day and his profound love for all types of animals."

She says the blessing of the animals is meant to give individuals with animals a chance to reflect on the positive connection that animals have to our

Photo by Mark Murray.

physical and emotional health. In recent years some people have brought sick animals. Some people are sick themselves and some people are grieving great loss.

"We minister to them all," she said.

On this glorious fall day we all stood under a covered portico of the medical building as Fr. Mieczyslaw Wit blessed each of us by name, sprinkled us with holy water and reminded everyone of the responsibility of humans to "give love, care, and respect to God's animals."

The blessing is given in honor of St. Francis of Assisi, who founded the Franciscan order in the 13th century. And while I'm not technically a member of the church no one seemed to mind.

Animals are by nature ecumenical (I'd be glad to go to a bark-mitzvah, if I were ever invited) . We really don't get in each other's way the way humans seem to.

We know we're all God's creatures and if we keep that uppermost in our minds, it seems to work out a lot easier that way for everyone.

While Saint Francis lived nearly 700 years ago, the blessing for the animals which is celebrated around the world is still largely the same.

"Blessed are you, Lord God, maker of all living creatures. You called forth fish in the sea, birds in the air and animals on the land. You inspired St. Francis to call all of them his brothers and sisters. We ask you to bless this pet. By the power of your love, enable it to live according to your plan. May we always praise you for all your beauty in creation. Blessed are you, Lord our God, in all your creatures! Amen."

To which, let me add, Amen.

All in all, it was a grand day. The sun shone, the air was clear. I shared blessings with Charlie, the retriever (a handsome devil); Randy, the greyhound (whose owner thinks he rescued him, we know it was the other way around); Louis the poodle, and Mia the cat ("she's family," said owners Charles and Doreen Douglas, and indeed she is). I received a nifty trinket reminding one and all that I had been blessed by the patron saint of animals and I was still home in time for my nap.

I can't say I felt very much different after the blessing. I'm still tempted by squirrels; I haven't lost the urge to roll around in the mud, and I'm still guilty of stealing a piece of cake if it's left too close to the end of the coffee table.

But I never said that I was perfect.

Just blessed.

DOG PARK

Generally, I look at dog parks about the same way my master looks at senior citizens centers. We don't brag about going, but we have fun once we get there.

In a perfect world, of course there wouldn't be dog parks, there would just be parks and woods, and trails where we could run freely, follow our noses, chase squirrels and meet up with our fellow canines for some good-natured cavorting, then be on our way.

But of course the world isn't quite perfect largely because - how shall I put this nicely - there are people in it, many of whom drive cars, play sports and sometimes like to walk about without bumping into strange dogs.

Go figure.

Frankly, I've always thought there are no strange dogs, just strange dog owners, but there seem to be enough of these around that reluctantly I agree there should probably be a place where like-minded dog lovers and their loving dogs can gather for some lighthearted play without fear of running afoul of leash laws (don't get me started) or venturing into perfectly good romping areas which for reasons unknown to me have been posted "no dogs allowed."

Humans, I must say, have been a little slow to grasp the point that it's hard to have it both ways. You can hardly be legislating us out of public places where so many of us and our owners would like to peacefully congregate without giving us a place to go.

And so I am proud to say I've noticed a number of dog parks around the region where we can spend some idle time doing what we do best: sniff each other, chase balls and generally act charming all in search of the universal canine compliment.

"Good dog."

And why, I wonder along with a certain New Yorker cartoonist, is it never "great dog?"

Be that as it may, dog parks seem to be an idea whose time has come and they seem to be sprouting like weeds, not that I have anything against weeds which I've found at times to be an excellent digestive tool especially after spending 20 minutes chewing on a stick.

Anyway, a typical day at the dog park will start with my master asking if I want to go to the p-a-r-k (he knows I always say yes; and why does he think I can't spell?)

There we meet up with all sorts (dogs and people) like the whippet who thinks he is a tight end, continually running down-and-out patterns waiting for someone to throw him a ball. Now, even though I'm a retriever, I don't get it. Throw the ball, fetch the ball, throw the ball; it seems so pointless. Not that I'm against pointlessness. Many of my favorite activities such as running after squirrels and chasing my tail are pointless, but at least they're pointless on my terms. Long ago, I trained my master that if he wants the darn ball so badly, he can get it himself.

Then there's the poodle who seems to think she's a cat, constantly giving me come-hither looks and then turning away like she couldn't care less. This behavior astonishes me. I'm used to being charming. Rejection confuses me. But it's like my master says, "poodles and cats, you can't really know what they're thinking."

Still, my favorite is the Great Dane who has turned slobbering into a high art. You wipe his mouth, he drools, you feed him, he drools some more. You say he's a good dog, he drools and slobbers. I've been known to slobber, of course, but no one slobbers as great as a Great Dane. I always say if you're only going to do one thing, do it well.

There's more of course. On some days I'll see a border collie (far too obedient to my taste; it makes the rest of us look bad) a Pekinese who thinks she's a St. Bernard and a boxer who is afraid of his own shadow.

On other days, it's just me and my master, and that's fine too. I hope he's not too d-i-s-a-p-p-o-i-n-t-e-d.

But if you're around, please drop by. And do me a favor. If my master throws you a ball, humor him and fetch.

You'll make his day.

BALL

It's often been said that a dog is man's best friend but at the risk of biting the hand that feeds me (not that I would ever do that) I must say that such friendship is at times a one-way street.

We love our humans of course, but the truth is they make rather untrustworthy friends.

I can't count of course, but if I could I couldn't count the number of times I am quietly anticipating (OK, jumping up and down) the prospect of accompanying my master on an adventure (and isn't everything an adventure) only to be told "not now" (whatever that means) and ordered to sit quietly (fat chance) until his return "soon" (another word not in the dog dictionary).

Add to that the indignity of all the restaurants, ball fields, supermarkets, public transit and government buildings where humans frequently gather with their so-called friends, yet where their putative "best friends" are generally not invited and the mere thought of their appearance sniffed at (not there's anything wrong with sniffing.)

Then of course there is the pesky matter of "work" (whatever that is) but which too seems to be a place that humans are often off to sans us.

I'm afraid it must be said that while humans can be fun for the weekend romp in the woods (if they don't get a better offer) and certainly appreciated at dinner time, their hectic schedules and odd notions of where we do and do not belong make them far too unreliable to occupy first place in the friend department.

For that we have balls.

While we love our masters, we are in love with our balls. Give a dog a ball and you have given him a friend for life.

A ball is never too tired to play, never too busy for fun and never running out the door leaving you behind. Balls are good natured -- willing to be fetched at all hours and unfazed at being left alone for days. They don't mind being gnawed on, buried and occasionally half-eaten in the name of doggy fun and have been known to wait patiently without complaint under snow all winter so they can be discovered in the spring.

Balls go where you go and stay where you left them and how many humans can you say that about? They are, in so many ways, a dog's dog.

So let humans bask in the delusion that they are a dog's best friend when dogs know better (as they usually do).

When you really want to have a ball; get a ball.

DIG

Whenever humans don't have much of a plan, they often say "if you build it, they will come."

But dogs, who never plan, have a much superior aphorism: "If you can dig it, then you can dig it."

I've always loved digging. There's something about the cool dirt in the paws as the soil gives way to whatever lies beneath. I suppose it's how certain humans feel about gardening minus the pesky seeding, planting, weeding, watering, waiting, fretting, flooding, drought, harvesting and grubs.

Not that I have anything against grubs or worms, or rabbits all of whom are perfectly fine denizens of the animal kingdom, and who all seem to recognize digging to be its own occupation and not preparatory to anything in particular. You never hear of grubs wreaking havoc on a hole the way they might to a garden and when I encounter any in my excavations, I simply nudge them aside with my nose and go on digging while they just keep on being, well, grubby.

Nor do I worry about all the disasters that Nature can deliver to a garden once it's planted. Dig a hole, get a hole. Never something else, which I consider nothing short of well, fantastic.

Holes are pure potential. While physicists may postulate that a black hole lets nothing in or out, a dog hole says "come on in." Like the sorts of curios that humans find at tag sales, once you dig one, you immediately find a use for it.

Most humans assume that dogs dig holes to bury bones, but that is the narrow view and not true in my case. When I get a bone, I chew it and chew it until there is just about nothing left to bury. And if I did happen to bury one, it wouldn't last long because just knowing that a bone was buried somewhere would be enough to make me want to dig it up immediately.

The kind of dog that can bury a bone and forget about it must be like the kind of human that can buy a gallon of ice cream and then forget it's in the freezer.

For me, burying a bone and leaving it is like saving for a rainy day and then realizing that every day is rainy.

Of course lots of things wind up in holes besides bones. Personally, I like burying socks, against the possibility that someday I might wake up and realize that I am barefoot and that this is a problem. Admittedly such a time is long off, but it's nice to know that should I ever want to start wearing socks, I'd have plenty to choose from.

Most of my dog toys also eventually wind up in the hole as they are of little use once I've ripped the stuffing out of them. I've always taken a rather French Revolution approach to my toys and a backyard burial seems only fitting for the legions of them I have beheaded, drawn and quartered and otherwise mutilated in the first 10 minutes after receiving them.

Of course I have to admit I sometimes dig holes because I just like digging holes. I suppose a psychiatrist would have a field day with this but one of the advantages of being a dog is that few of us go in for counseling. And while my master will sometimes come along and fill up the freshly dug hole (what would a psychiatrist say about that) I take it in the way he takes me returning a fetched ball – as a sign he wants me to do it again.

So I do, prompting him to speculate out loud whether I was planning on digging my way to China. Of course I have no idea where China is but I suspect I would have to dig only halfway there. Because somewhere in China there is very likely a dog digging himself halfway to me.

BARK

Every so often I will hear my master trying to assure a fearful stranger who has misunderstood my usual glad-to-meet-you greeting with the warm words that my bark is worse than my bite.

Well, I should hope so, as biting (with the exception perhaps of some biting sarcasm) is at all times the farthest thing from my mind. Biting is a bad business for both human and canine and best confined to the dinner table where it can perform its proper role of effectively getting morsels from plate to gullet as efficiently as possible. Sure, the occasional puppy might take the occasional nibble from his master (along with furniture, dog toys and anything else around the house) but soon enough everyone learns there are far more effective ways to communicate.

Not that we wouldn't talk if we could, although I've observed that having language and communicating effectively are hardly the same thing. Still, the creator of all things has seen fit to give us only limited vocal abilities so we are forced to make do with the sounds we have.

Human babies know this instinctively as they navigate their first year with a limited range of sounds, relying on human parents (who are generally clueless about the job) to decipher a wet cry from a hungry cry from a sleepy cry. Eventually children learn more and more words until they arrive at adolescence where they again limit their spoken interactions with their parents to some version of "give me money" along with the single vocabulary word of "whatever."

Barking is another matter entirely and I must say that I am rather proud of mine, firm but sensitive; authoritative yet ultimately non-threatening. So I believe it is time to state clearly that my bark is not simply worse than my bite.

It is far better.

With a single bark and a slight nudge I can greet my master while he is yet abed reminding him of first light and time for breakfast (mine, not his, I don't care when he eats). A slightly more insistent bark can be employed for emphasis should he choose to roll over (a trick of inordinate interest to humans) in an effort to stay half asleep, a condition unknown to dogs as we are either all asleep or all awake.

A different more formal bark is called for when time to "do my business" conveying the consequences of noncompliance, and a more playful one upon encountering fellow canines in woods or park. Occasionally I will test the waters of a canine acquaintance by delivering a low growl along with my characteristic crouch until I've determined his true intentions. But once convinced of his friendly nature, I will bark conversationally until it is time to go.

My afternoon is often spent lolling on my front porch where I bark pleadingly with postal workers, delivery men and service providers in hopes of getting a friendly pat on the head, cadging an occasional dog treat and fishing (not there's anything wrong with fish) for the universal canine compliment of "good dog."

More menacing types might get something that sounds snarlish but which is strictly for show. My watchdog status ends pretty much with watching. After that it's a job for the security system.

By evening time a simple bark is enough to summon dinner and my bedtime bark is more of a purr although I never would admit it to the cats of my acquaintance, who in any case, couldn't care less.

So there you have it – wake up bark, breakfast bark, business bark, park bark, stranger bark, fishing bark, dinner bark and nighty-night bark.

In short, a bark for all occasions and all without the pesky use of words that can so easily be misunderstood, and each one better than my bite.

Much better.

CATALOGUES

Most of my contact with the postal service is on a personal, not professional basis. I give the mailman my big eyes, meaning it's OK to drop off the day's post for my cohabitants and he in turn takes his finger off the dog spray and offers me a biscuit. No stamps needed; no postage due.

Rarely is there anything in the mail for me, which I never really minded, or even thought about before. Dogs live a contained life. We meet all our friends in the woods, correspond through barking, don't incur bills and are never audited, which near as I can tell accounts for most of the mail humans receive. Still, I was thrilled recently to get my first piece of real mail – from Doctors Foster and Smith whose actual medical credentials may be suspect, but who nevertheless had my interests at heart as evidenced by the photographs of dogs looking just like me having what appeared to be a grand time cavorting through nearly every page of the 100-page catalogue.

OK, so technically, the catalogue was junk mail but since it came by post I figure I was still doing my part for the beleagured postal service which has lately definitely acquired underdog status and I am always for the underdog. Technically it was addressed to resident, but as I spend more time around here than my masters and as no one in the house would have any use for the hundreds of items advertised I have to assume that the intended audience was…well, me.

Who else would have any use for the pharmacopia of products designed to rid me of ticks, soften my skin, freshen my breath and soothe my aching joints. Who else could use the grooming aids to clip, trim, comb, brush or do my eyebrows (wait, I like my eyebrows). Who knew I had so many fashion options in vests (navy, green, plum and my favorite, periwinkle,) or sweatshirts, slickers, hoodies and get this - goggles. How about the fifteen different kinds of toys which I'll wreck the minute I get them. Why not just sell the little noise maker inside and be done with it?

I admit it was heady stuff, and yet, there was a dark side. I'm not talking about the leashes, the cages, the harnesses and the muzzles offering greater control (I control myself thank you.) Or the collars masquerading as a fashion statement, but actually containing enough voltage to not only get my attention but jolt me into submission if I didn't come running. How positively medieval.

I just couldn't shake the vague sense that whatever I got from the catalogue would never be enough. If I got a vest, wouldn't I want a hoodie. If I got a slicker, would I be any slicker? How soon after I get my personal aviator goggles does it occur to someone to push me out of a plane.

Oh, I had trouble, right here in catalogue city. I could feel it in the pit of my stomach when I read about the 22 different doggie cures for heartburn and gas the deramaxx, previxoc, carpaquin, novox cosequin, the duralactin advertisements made my hips hurt not to mention my tongue twist. Why exactly would I stock up with "ear care essentials," when licking seemed to be fine.

The more I thumbed (OK, pawed) through the catalogue the simple truth of catalogue shopping became obvious. The more I saw, the more I wanted. The more I wanted, the worse I felt. All of a sudden, what I really wanted was to be back in the woods, no vest, no goggles, no ear essentials. I'd take my chances with the ticks.

Obviously there was only one thing to do with the Doctors Foster and Smith veterinarian guaranteed catalogue.

And it was tasty too.

VET

I generally avoid reading articles about dogs not so much because I can't read (after all, I can't write, and yet here we are) but because the humans that write such articles often seem so clueless.

But I couldn't avoid a recent story about an Idaho veterinarian who attended a national conference in Florida to present his ideas for a fear-free approach to veterinary care, which included such notions as pastel scrubs instead of white; yoga mats instead of cold examination tables; and piped in classical music all designed to improve the "veterinary experience."

Well, good luck with that. Most of the dogs I know consider a veterinary experience the way they consider a "kennel" experience -- not exactly the end of the world, but no cause for celebration and a sure sign that the real fun lies elsewhere. Add to that the sharp objects, general probing and the often high pitched whining that is commonplace at most office visits and few dogs of my acquaintance would confuse a trip to the vet with a romp in the woods.

And why should we be any different than humans in this regard? Truly, how many humans wake up each morning and say to themselves, "I think I'll visit the doctor today for a quality medical experience. Wouldn't that be fun?"

The fact is that even the thought of visiting a health care professional, human or canine, is often enough to bring on a rash of symptoms. Physicians are well acquainted with the "white-coat" effect that can raise the blood pressure and send the pulse soaring among even the most rational patients. How much worse must it be for dogs who – regardless of any yoga mats or classical music that may lie within -- can smell the vet all the way from the parking lot.

Now none of this is personal. It's my experience that vets love animals (why else would they go into the business) and I'm sure that many of them are good citizens and kind to the animals they call their own. It's just that I've always preferred to view my vet the way I view abstract art – from a distance. And while I can rationally say that I like them "as people" (as opposed to say, voles,) as vets they inspire in me, the same feeling I imagine I inspire in squirrels, which is "time to head for the hills."

Not that there's anything wrong with hills, which in many ways are infinitely more relaxing than the average veterinary office, festooned with diagrams of anatomically correct lookalikes of my species except all their organs are on the outside.

No one in the hills is trying to push me onto a scale and scrunching their nose at the one or two pounds I may have gained in recent months as a result from some artful begging at the table. No one in the hills is poking around my belly looking for lumps the way a prospector might pan for gold and upon finding one pronouncing it "probably benign" whatever that means. And no one in the hills is suggesting that some foul smelling medicine be pawned off in a piece of deli turkey, a trick made no less dastardly by the fact that I fall for it *every* time.

Imagine if you will that the examination tables were turned and it was the humans who were led in on a leash to an examination room surrounded by strange smells and cold hands and asked to "calm down" as a white-coated dog with a furrowed brow announces that whatever happens next "won't hurt."

Won't hurt indeed. As if the inspections and the injections are a walk in the park (not that there's anything wrong with that) and simply for my own good in the long run (not that there's anything wrong with that either) all designed to insure I live a long life, a comment that is hardly relaxing for a species whose idea of the future barely extends beyond the next five minutes.

And so we canines at the very least can be excused if – Mozart aside – we don't embrace a visit to the vet and if we doubt that the presence of a yoga mat or a pink lab coat is likely to turn our well-founded dread into the canine equivalent of Disneyland. We know that our masters have our best interests at heart when they load us into the car and say we are "going for a ride." But as a species that prides itself on knowing fun when we see it, don't expect us to jump for joy when the vet walks into the room.

We'd rather just jump.

DOG CLASS

If it's Wednesday then it's time for dog class.

Now some humans believe that dogs have no sense of time which is not quite accurate.

It's true that we're not so great about remembering the exact dates of the Spanish American War or precisely how long we've been in Afghanistan but that's because we had no dogs in those fights. But ask us when it's close to dinner, or when we'd like to go out and we get like commuters waiting on the train platform for the 6:07 to pull in.

So you don't have to ask me where we're going Wednesday nights when my master gathers up my treats, and my leash and points me toward the car.

It's dog class.

Now technically it's dog obedience class but I prefer not to think of it that way, since the name is really kind of insulting, with its implication that I may be coming up slightly short in that department. I like to think I'm obedient like certain Hollywood starlets are faithful – in our way.

For example, I tend to take a certain lawyer-like approach to commands such as "come." I'm coming in the way spring is – eventually. Or like my mistress arrives at a dinner party – when she's good and ready. Or when my master is cutting the grass – when he feels like it but probably after the next inning. The fact is that "come" doesn't always mean now. It might be more like the preparation of fine wine – not before its time.

Not to mention that some commands are downright silly.

Why would I want to shake your hand? Do you know how many germs humans carry?

Roll over? Why bother?

Play dead? That's just weird.

Then there are the commands which evoke the response of Bartleby the

Scrivener in the Melville story: a simple "I'd rather not."

"Fetch," I'd rather not, get it yourself.

"Drop that stick." Why should I?

"Don't jump on the bed or you're in trouble." An obviously empty threat.

"Don't chase that squirrel." Fat chance.

Still, I recognize that some of the commands are for my own safety, such as watch out for cars, as if I haven't seen all the road kill out there. And I suppose there's always some room for improvement, so if my master wants to take me for a ride to meet other dogs and get treats in return for humoring him then I say "why not, let's go."

And so we go.

One of the things I like most about dog class is that I get rewarded for hardly doing anything. Call me over, I get a treat. Call me again, treat again. Tell me to stay, I stay. Treat again.

Not exactly heavy lifting.

And sometimes I get a treat just for being me. "Good dog," they say over and over.

As if I didn't know.

Now I can't exactly say that I'm exactly at the top of dog class. That dubious honor seems to belong to the border collies who take commands so well that I wonder about their childhood.

I once saw a collie that was told to stay and did so for an hour without moving a paw, which I suppose is good if you're trying out for a wax museum, but which to my way of thinking isn't exactly doglike.

And although I admit I can't hold a candle to a collie I'm practically Einstein compared to this bloodhound that seems to think that stop means slobber and stay means slobber, and halt means slobber and wait means… you get the picture.

I'm sure he's perfectly good as a private investigator, but I sure wouldn't want him for my lawyer.

So, I'm pretty happy with my place smack in the middle (OK, upper middle) of the class, smart enough to get by but in no danger of being a know-it-all. Living around humans has taught me that it's very possible to be too smart for your own good.

Charm, I believe, works much better.

AKC

I noticed that more than 751 dogs and their handlers were in town last week for an American Kennel Club Working Breed dog show and I wasn't one of them.

Now, despite my aversion to any organization with the word 'Kennel" in its name, I have nothing against dog shows. Canines are a tolerant lot and if our masters want to travel all over the country to show us off, I say "fine," but I find I get just as much high praise and attention from a brisk walk through the campus of an all-girls school.

I suspect that the average dog looks at dog shows about the same way as the average human looks at the Oscars - interesting from a distance, but not to be confused with real life.

That's because (and I don't believe I'm revealing any great secret here) a dog show is an activity that is much more attractive to people than it is to dogs.

To determine if this is so, try this simple test: Would a dog do it if no people were around? It is no great philosophical question to ask: if a dog spotted a squirrel in the woods and there were no humans around, would he still give chase? Of course. Ditto for chewing on a stick, tail chasing or digging for voles. But would a dog on his own come up with the idea of giving up a perfectly good Saturday afternoon to travel hours by car (OK, maybe that part isn't so bad if the window is open), only to be leashed and packed into a crowded arena and led around a white fenced ring to be judged based on agility and presentation?

I don't think so.

Now I know that this might sound like sour grapes (not that there's anything wrong with that, although I'm not supposed to eat them) because golden retrievers almost never win these competitions and are often not even allowed to enter.

Handlers wait in the ring with some of the 48 Golden Retrievers competing. The 2020 Westminster Dog Show held at Pier 94 in Manhattan. Tuesday, February 11, 2020. New York, NY USA (Aristide Economopoulos | NJ Advance Media)

The recent "working breed" show included 27 breeds such as Great Danes, Doberman Pinschers, Siberian Huskies, giant Schnauzers and black Russian Terriers without even a whiff at retrievers who were presumably too busy chasing balls and not necessarily returning them to be considered "working" which the judges define as guarding property, pulling sleds and performing water rescues. The dogs, according to the judges, do not even compete against each other, but against a standard "blueprint for the breed."

Well la-di-da, which is dog talk for la-di-da. I've never seen my blueprint (although I suspect it would be tasty), and I have my own standards which often include rolling in the snow or just sitting around and doing nothing. While it's true that I don't regularly pull sleds or perform water rescues (I doubt these show dogs do either; they're too busy running around in circles past make-believe fences), it's because I am too busy bringing smiles to the faces of young children, a competition I would gladly pit myself against any Doberman Pinscher you can name.

As Groucho Marx's dog once remarked, "I'm not interested in any club that would accept me as a member." But should you ever hear of a dog show in which there are no leashes, no handlers, no judges, no blueprints and no standards, feel free to send me an engraved invitation.

But don't expect me to come.

My master would rather watch the Oscars, and I'll be busy napping.

BRONZE AGAIN

The American Kennel Club has once again released its list of most popular purebred canines and for the 27th year golden retrievers came up (drum roll please…)

Bronze.

Again. And again. And at the risk of sounding repetitive (why not, that's the whole point) 25 more agains. Once more I'm left wagging my tail (nothing wrong with that) behind Labrador retrievers, German shepherds and just a whisker ahead (not that there's anything wrong with whiskers) of -- get this -- the French bulldog.

Not that I care of course. OK, a little. You bet.

It's just that after 27 years of trying for the brass ring what I keep getting is so, well, brass, not to mention plain old predictable. And for a breed that prides itself on unpredictability (even I don't know what I'm going to do next) another barely in the money finish just sticks in my craw (and I don't even have one.)

I mean Kennel Club third place is nothing to sniff at (as if there's anything wrong with sniffing) especially considering the source whose prize winners would likely never be caught dead in any kennel that I've ever seen the inside of, and whose owners routinely give up a brisk romp in the woods for a "fun" (by which I mean boring) leashed up outing walking in a circle in a crowded arena without a squirrel in sight.

I suppose that with a bit of imagination (not that hard for a breed that imagines it can outrun a rabbit), I guess you might say that bronze is sort of gold, but then again that's the problem isn't it? To have a heart of gold, and a coat of gold to be constantly reminded that two out of three humans might pass us over in favor of a non-golden doggy in a window that I can assure you has never been to Labrador and a German whose shepherding days are well behind him is practically un-American.

Maybe someone will build a wall.

Never mind, I don't mean it. Dogs would never stoop so low (with four legs I doubt it's even anatomically possible). Did I mention the French bull-dog that is yapping at my heels?

You get the picture, and it's not a pretty one.

Where exactly did my breed go wrong? Haven't we always sat by the door waiting to greet our master as if he had come back from the 100-year-war even though he's just gone out for a quart of milk. Don't we still hang our head out of the car's rear window (and never complain about sitting in the back) as if we are going to the circus when in fact we're just going to the vet? Don't we line up each morning and night for the same exact meal we had the day before and wolf it down (not that there's anything wrong with wolves, some of my favorite ancestors still run in packs) as if our supper bowl were Zagat rated? And don't we still turn heads at every rest stop along the highway and accept high praise from complete strangers who wish they had brought their dog along (why don't they?)

Really, what more can we do?

And yet.

I suppose I can take solace in the fact that I did finish ahead of the beagles, (take that, Snoopy), poodles, Rottweilers, Yorkshire terriers and German shorthaired pointers (didn't his mother teach him it's not polite to point) and the roughly 340 other dog breeds bringing up the rear of canine society.

But third. Again. Really it's all so boring. And boring is one thing I definitely am not.

So, maybe next year. In the meantime, a word to the wiseguy Labradors and Shepherds. Do you hear that sound behind you?

It's me. And I'm coming.

AS YEARS GO BY

THEO

ANOTHER BIRTHDAY

Today is my birthday and my master is reading the obituary pages.

I'm not making a big deal of the connection (OK, maybe a little deal, or medium, or what Starbucks calls Grande, which means medium/large. But not quite Venti, whatever that means.)

It's just that these days he's been reading the obituary page more frequently (OK, every morning). When he was more of a pup, he never read obituaries at all, skipping straight to sports. Over the years he might glance at them casually after carefully poring over the news and editorial pages on the way to the day's advice from dear Abby.

Dear Abby, my dog keeps circling the dinner bowl every afternoon. What is he trying to tell us?

Seriously?

Anyway, now my master pretty much goes straight to the obituary pages and then on to the comics where his favorite is Peanuts because after nearly 500 dog years, the characters haven't aged a day and the strip keeps appearing even though its human creator has been dead for decades.

All of which is a rather roundabout observation (when you're a dog, everything is roundabout, why do you think we chase our tails) that except on the funny pages life keeps moving forward unless you're a comic strip dog who happens to be a World War I ACE fighter plane pilot. And whether it's your birthday or not, if you start each morning reading the obituary pages and you are not among the headlines, you can safely figure you're not dead.

Yet.

Dogs do not regularly appear in the obituary pages but that doesn't mean we are unaware of the passage of time, or of our absurdly short life span. Humans are not particularly helpful in this regard by reminding us that one of our years is seven of theirs, often expressing our age in people years which we find mildly depressing but accept gamely enough from a species who think nothing of subtracting years from their own age upon reaching the far side of 50.

We catch the gray in our face when drinking from streams and notice the ache in our hips that follows a romp in the woods.

We notice when a dog we've seen regularly around the park doesn't show up anymore. And we've all heard about dogs that go into the vet's office and don't come out.

And we hear things. Like the grandfather who helped his grandson pack a going away box for the ailing pet so he would have a ball, and biscuit when the day came for the one-way trip to the vet.

Or a dog of my acquaintance, "Scamp," who after 17 years wasn't doing much scamping anymore and instead spent his day making smaller and smaller circles around the house.

Dear Abby: My dog can hardly walk, and won't eat. He sleeps most of the day and cries at night. What is he trying to tell us?

Seriously?

All of which sounds like a pretty dour way to celebrate a birthday. And for a dog whose default position is cheerful I think I'll ignore the fact that my master is reading obituary pages and tug on him until he realizes it's time for a walk.

If you can take a walk, you're not dead.

Yet.

Happy eighth birthday to me.

BIRTHDAY PARTIES

You say it's your birthday…We're gonna have a good time - Paul McCartney/ John Lennon, 1968.

I hear it's my birthday. Again.

And although I can't much say that I enjoy being reminded of that by a pair of beetles (not that I have anything against beetles, although who are they to talk, their life spans are astonishingly short even by dog standards, not to mention the ever-present threat of being squashed just for getting into an opened bag of flour -- hardly my idea of a good time) there really seems to be no ignoring the fact that my birthday has arrived, ready or not.

Generally, my birthday (Sept. 27, to be exact) is marked by a wave of nostalgia of how fast time has flown since my appearance in the household a mere seven years ago. This leads to the inevitable calculations that in human years I am actually 49, (one dog year equaling seven human ones) an odd way to bring about birthday cheer. Imagine reminding humans of their age in dinosaur or elephant years and the growl that might elicit in return.

Never mind. Dogs are magnanimous, and if humans want to calculate my age by multiples of seven let them count away (my counting skills get fuzzy after two anyway.) The point is that I am now a middle-aged dog and while you won't find me buying a sports car, or running away with a dog half my age I am not above a bit of reflection about the passage of my years.

All in all it's been a good ride (or half a ride; hopefully less than half) I arrived in the household just about the time the last child departed and just in time to lift the general gloom that sometimes descends upon human empty nesters (birds don't mind at all; they beat wings straight to Florida).

My masters who seemed oddly unaware of the illogic of not getting a dog when the kids were little for fear that they would wind up taking care of it, were now fully embracing the thought of caring for one now that the kids had skedaddled. And while they were pathetically unschooled in the ways of puppydom, I was patient but firm in training them to walk, feed and pet me so that in short order I was pretty much running things around here, evicting one of my humans from his favorite chair, and eliciting chorus after chorus of good dog from the other even for doing such un-good yet dog-like things as scratching on the door or chewing up the furniture.

How fast time flies when you're chewing. Season followed season and the days of cavorting through the snow, the leaves, and the streams have morphed into a slow trot (not that there's anything wrong with metamorphosis, some of my best friends are butterflies.) Squirrels are in even less danger than they used to be and if I look too long in a mirror (a dicey proposition at any age) I can see a flecks of white where the golden used to be.

So it goes. Unbeknownst to me, one of the compelling reasons my masters got me in their later years was so that we would march into the twilight together. By their calculations (I never calculate, no good comes of it) we will reach 70 at the same time.

But we are not there yet. Until then, I count my age the way I want to count. (don't we all.)

Today, I am only 7.

Happy birthday to me. We're gonna have a good time.

Wait and see.

STEP

I hate to admit it but I appear to have lost a step.

Not that humans would notice. I'm sure to them I still take off like a rocket after passing squirrels, bound effortlessly over field and stream, and coming running at dinner time like the menu isn't exactly the same as the day before.

But I know.

I know the squirrels seem like they've been working out while I feel like I'm running in mud (not that there's anything wrong with that.)

And I know I'm just as fast for the first 50 yards as I ever was; it's just those 50 yards seem a lot farther than they ever were.

Not that it should matter much for a species that lives mostly on charm. I mean, we're not wolves anymore. We don't have to kill what we eat and I could lose another 1,000 steps and still keep up with humans most of whom seem to amble through life without breaking a sweat.

And in the long run (which is getting longer all the time) what difference does it make if I'm a step slower in chasing after a squirrel that I'll never catch anyway and wouldn't know what to do with if I did.

But the thorny question remains, well like a thorn picked up in the woods. Just exactly where did that step go to, and how might I get it back?

Now these are the exact philosophical questions that keep humans up at night (and who would want that?) It's like seeing the first gray hair (coincidentally I've seen a few of those, what can it all mean?) or suddenly being aware of your hips.

Dogs like to take each day as it comes and if that day comes with an achy hip then maybe it means I should lie down for a while until it feels better.

Still, something that is lost can perhaps be found and if that's the case, then I better start looking.

I started with my collection of human socks gleaned from the laundry. If humans feel the need to keep putting their feet in them perhaps they left a step behind at bed time.

No luck. Next I tried the various holes I have dug around the yard to see if a step had just stepped into one the way humans are always dropping their keys.

Again, nothing. Finally I searched around my dog bowl figuring that sooner or later good things show up there.

Alas and alack (although I did feel a bit better just using a phrase that does not regularly come up in dog conversation – we generally "alack" for nothing.)

What more could I do? Perhaps I had lost the step on vacation, or in the wood, or at the park. Retracing one's steps is not easy to do for a species graced with four legs (just which steps would I retrace?) a strong wanderlust and a weak memory. I had to face the fact that I had taken just about all the steps a dog could reasonably take and not found the one I was looking for.

I guess I'll just to have get used to getting where I'm going one step later than I used to. Who knows? Perhaps the squirrels will wait.

GRAY

Generally speaking, we dogs don't care much for mirrors.

For one we're never sure what we are seeing. Is that handsome dog looking back at me friend or foe. Should I jump inside the mirror and play or crouch down and see if he comes to me.

And not to wax too philosophical; but if he is me, then who am I?

Ditto for still water, aluminum foil and freshly cleaned windows. Upon reflection, I don't like reflection. Much better I think to avoid the who am I/ who is he thing which no matter how I look at it makes my head swim (not that there's anything wrong with swimming.)

And it's not that I (or any dog) really care about looks. When you come right down to it, dogs are dogs and you seldom hear one saying the other needs to lose a few pounds or get his hair done, or even could use a bath. That's human stuff. Of course with the exception of babies, even the homeliest of us get more compliments on our looks than your average human, so much so that my master has finally come to realize that whenever a comely female passerby stops to exclaim "you're so beautiful" she is *always* talking to me.

So imagine my surprise when despite my general disinclination toward reflection, I happened to catch a glimpse of myself in the car's rear view mirror and notice that I had been replaced practically overnight by an albino version of myself.

OK, maybe not a complete albino, but mixed in with all the glorious golden fur there was no getting around it -- I was going white. Sure, it was only a few white hairs but where there's one there's sure to be another and before you know it there would be a polar bear at my dinner dish and the bear would be me.

Of course there's nothing wrong with polar bears if you happen to live in the North Pole and you started out white. But imagine if a polar bear started turning golden and wanted to chase squirrels, where would he be then?

OK, maybe that wouldn't be so bad since morphing into a golden retriever is a lot better than morphing out of one. Not that I have anything against caterpillars but I never met one who wanted to go back once he was a butterfly. Timeless beauty may not be everything, but it's easy to get used to.

And I was certainly not about to get used to that single white hair, which I suspect was like a single snowflake -- you never notice the first ones coming down and then suddenly, the woods are full of them. And while there can be a certain beauty about a forest full of snow, most dogs know there is a lot less wildlife around in the winter and we'd rather not think about where they've all gone.

Of course I've seen golden retrievers go white before but usually these are old dogs stumbling around on arthritic hips and no longer even interested in chasing squirrels. And despite my recent birthday which catapulted me into dog middle age, I consider myself still a pup with lots of cavorting, romping and dashing left in me.

So what's a golden-plus-one-white-hair retriever to do?

I suppose if I were human I could comb over my white hair, or dye it, or do what most humans do which pretend it's not there. But that would be silly and decidedly undoggish. Better to embrace my whiteness as a sign of growing wisdom. Surely I can be playful and distinguished; puppy-like and august (that should keep the winter of my discontent at bay).

Perhaps an old(er) dog can learn new tricks and the first one should be that one white hair does not an old dog make. When all is said and done I still have a heart of gold, and upon reflection, no mirror in the world can change that.

WEIGHT

Weight watchers of the world eat your hearts out (I wonder how many points THAT is?)

I am the biggest loser.

While there is usually not much good news that comes out of a trip to the veterinarian (how excited can you get over a rabies shot?) I am proud to say that at my semi-annual weigh-in I tipped the scales at five pounds less than my usual fighting weight (a human figure of speech, -- I would never do any real fighting.)

But the weight loss was real and apparently significant to the vet who at recent visits had taken to nagging my masters that I was getting just a tad chunky (not that anyone asked me, personally I figure if chunky is good enough for peanut butter, it's good enough for me.)

Naturally, I denied the problem, reasoning that more of me just meant more of me to love and that just as you would never see me pointing out to my master that he had been spending a bit too much time at the bakery, I might expect the same courtesy of him.

Still the evidence (not to mention the poundage) had been mounting that a dog my age (as if I could do anything about that) could stand to lose a few pounds lest the added strain go straight to my hips (it's always the hips, isn't it ladies?) And while I may believe that appearing a bit more Reubenesque might add to my charms, my added girth could bring on the joint problems that seem to particularly affect my breed (no doubt a result of all that swagger that I must say comes naturally.)

As if any of this were my fault.

It's not exactly that I control the meal times around here. I show up pretty regularly at my dog dish at the appointed hour and eat whatever is placed before me, which generally appears in the exact amount and formulation of the meal from the day before. Add to that the small amount I claim by invoking the 10-second rule toward anything dropped from the table, and the limited rations I can beg by displaying my considerable charm to guests, and it is easy to see that whatever responsibility might exist for a few extra pounds lies elsewhere.

I mean, it's not like I can open the refrigerator door around here, an event that seems to occur so regularly and at all hours that you might think the humans in the household were practicing for the Olympics.

I, in turn, figured I was doing my part by jumping at the chance for exercise whenever possible and chasing after squirrels in the hopes that while the chances of success were slim, perhaps the calorie expenditure would lighten my spirits.

And while it is true that I seldom turned down treats, I chalked such behavior up to my general politeness and the seeming pleasure humans derived from not eating alone.

After all, who am I to throw stones (not that there's anything wrong with stones.) So I was glad to add the sound of the refrigerator opening to the list of things that get my attention. And if my hovering should elicit a small contribution, who was I to refuse?

Still, I noticed that the handouts were getting thin around here, in hopes no doubt that such thinning was contagious, which apparently was the case as the scales don't lie, much as humans seem to sometimes wish they would.

And I must say when I saw the general cause for celebration that the loss of a few pounds occasioned around the house, I was glad to join in figuring that perhaps that somewhere, however illogically there might be some treat in it for me.

But alas no, as I was to learn that apparently losing weight was to be its own reward and to be named the biggest loser in the family, was now suddenly a good thing.

Which was fine with me, because I eat up praise just about as enthusiastically as I do table scraps.

BALTo

If, as humans like to believe, middle age is a time to come to grips with all the things that one will never be, then now that I'm 7 (49 in human midlife crisis time, still not too late to get a sports car) I guess I'm going to have to face the fact that I will never be Balto.

For the few humans ignorant of both canine and Alaskan history, Balto was the daring sled dog who in 1925 braved his way through hundreds of miles of frozen tundra in 60-below-zero temperatures to deliver life- saving medicine to the village of Nome whose children were clinging to life in the midst of a diphtheria outbreak.

At the time, such an act of dog heroism was celebrated with a Hollywood contract, a nine-month vaudeville tour and a bronze statue of Balto which can be seen to this day in New York's Central Park where an outbreak of diphtheria is unlikely and where an inch of snow is enough to bring the entire city to a staggering halt.

Closer to home, Balto's race to glory went on to inspire the Alaskan Iditarod Sled dog race, an odd sort of celebration, which one might think would feature dogs riding in the sled rather than pulling it, but that's what you get when you leave humans in charge of history.

The point is that I always fancied a bit of Balto in myself and for years harbored the notion that placed in similar circumstances (Alaska, sub-zero temperatures, thousands of miles of wilderness and wheezing children awaiting my arrival) that I too would leave the comfort of my sofa and dinner bowl and head north into history.

Until I realized that I *hate* the cold.

Not in small doses of course. For five or ten minutes I can romp through the snow with Labradors and Siberian Huskeys, shake the snow off my fur and head back for more. But just as my fellow snow dogs are hearing the

call of the wild, I am hearing the call of the living room and reminding myself that the great indoors with its central heating, dog blanket and fluffy stuffed toys has a certain charm and warmth of its own.

I am reminded of all this during the last week when back-to-back snowstorms prompted my human cohabitants to don jackets and scarves (a preparation conveniently forgotten when it came to me) and head outside for some fun in the snow. Yet, when I reached my usual five minute-max of snow cavorting and headed straight for the door I was somehow accused of being a stick-in-the-mud (not that there's anything wrong with that).

It's not exactly that I am anti-snow; it's more that I am pro-warmth.

Being dry isn't bad either.

I suppose I could learn to love the snow, but then again with three other seasons why bother? And so I am just going to have to come to grips with the fact that the next time the call goes out for a dog of the north to trudge one thousand miles through sub-zero weather to deliver life threatening medicine this dog of the south is going to suggest one-day free delivery by drone.

It's not exactly the stuff of legend, but it makes me feel warm inside.

TIME

Of all the silly things humans do (and believe me the list is a long one) the silliest is the twice a year ritual of messing with time.

No dog would ever do this, and it's not just that we can't tell time in the conventional sense. We know when to get up, when to go to sleep, when to answer the call of nature (a human term -- we just call it pooping) and when it's time for dinner.

How much more do you need to know?

But humans can't seem to leave well enough alone, disrupting the space time continuum every November and March in a futile attempt to "save daylight."

Who knew that daylight needed saving. Was it kidnapped? Trapped in mine collapse? And how exactly might you save daylight anyway? In a bottle? In a bank account? Under a mattress?

It's all too confusing and the kind of thing that makes my head hurt, which any dog will tell you means it's time for a nap, which I'm now afraid to do because I might wake up in an hour that's been pushed back and find I've gotten no sleep at all!

Not many humans know it but daylight saving time was first invented (can you invent time?) by Benjamin Franklin's dog in 1784 and then sensibly forgotten until 1895 when an entomologist from New Zealand proposed a two-hour daylight saving shift. That idea too was quickly and sensibly dismissed until Germany implemented it in 1916 presumably in order to give soldiers more daylight for world conquest.

Ask any German shepherd how that worked out.

Nevertheless humans have clung to the notion that saving time is not only possible but a good idea even though any dog could point out the foolishness of such an endeavor with a well-known canine riddle: How many legs would a dog have if you called its tail a leg?

The answer for dimwitted humans is four. It doesn't matter what you call something if it's actually something else. I could call poison ivy a rose as my master walked through it, but I wouldn't be surprised when he started scratching.

Not to mention that this whole messing with time business opens up a can of worms (not that there's anything wrong with worms.)

Once you start losing an hour here and gaining one there, how long would it take before the power to alter time runs amok? My master for example would just as soon lose the entire eighth grade; his senior prom; and the summer his girlfriend broke his heart. The president might choose to lose the last decade in Afghanistan and Iraq and just wake up in the morning with the billions of dollars spent there back in the treasury. The Red Sox would pretty much like to declare baseball season saving time on all of 2014, and push the clock ahead to spring training.

But they can't and fooling around with the laws of physics just so school kids don't have to wait in the dark for the bus seems a bit extreme. At the end of the day, there's still only 24 hours in the day. This whole daylight savings time legerdemain sounds like robbing Peter to pay Paul, and while I've never met either of them, I doubt the arrangement works out too well for either of them.

Much better, I think, to just go to sleep when nature says so and wake up when it's time. A one-hour nap will take one hour no matter how hard anyone tries to save it.

Doing anything else is like chasing after what you've decided is a five-legged dog.

When you catch up to it, its tail is still its tail.

BEYOND

As this nation's only regularly appearing canine columnist, I'd like to think there is just about no dog-related topic on which I have no opinion.

Leash laws -- too Big Brother (not that I have anything against big brothers.) Besides, I happen to know plenty of living beings in need of leashes and few of them are dogs.

No dogs in restaurants? You don't hear me barking about annoying humans and I'd put up any dog I know against any baby in the house. Not to mention that it is perfectly acceptable etiquette to put a dog and a water bowl on the floor at an outdoor eatery and everyone thinks it's charming. Try that with a child.

Dogs prohibited in banks, supermarkets, buses, planes, athletic fields? Don't get me started.

Now as a professional holder of opinions, I try to never let the facts slow down anything that happens to catch my admittedly fleeting attention.

If there's one thing I've learned from my human colleagues, it's that there is nothing like some pesky fact to take the steam out of a really good opinion and so (like skunks) they are best given a wide berth in the hopes that they will amble away to bother someone else.

It's like going into a house where dogs and cats live together and discovering that they actually get along and the dog doesn't have to sleep with one eye open (which I imagine would be pretty inconvenient considering how much dogs sleep.)

All of which is a rather round-about way of saying (not that columnists have a problem with that) that I have absolutely no opinion whatsoever on Massachusetts House Bill 3272.

For those readers who have been too busy having a life to keep up with the machinations of human legislators, House Bill 3272 would allow cemeteries to set aside land in which deceased humans could be buried along with their beloved deceased pets.

Now since this is literally a life and death matter, (a phrase columnists use much too loosely) one might think it would call forth an opinion from a canine columnist (not that anyone asked) but try as I might I can't seem to conjure up a stand on lying six feet under.

On the one hand I would be close to my master for eternity.

On the other, I'd be, well, dead.

Now for a species with an absurdly short life span (spare me your comments, goldfish!), you might think we'd all be constantly thinking about what lies beyond the great beyond.

But we don't. For we have been given what most truly evolved humans spend their entire (and absurdly long) lives trying to achieve, which is the ability to live in the present.

Ask about what happens in the next life and we're most likely to ask for a walk right now. Try enlisting our aid in finding a misplaced leash and we will just jump up and down at the sound of the word "leash." Tell us you're leaving and that you will be back "soon" and we honestly have no idea what you are talking about.

If pressed, we might say that we've never been in charge of anything in this life and it's worked out pretty well; so why should we expect to know (or worry) about the next one.

The closest thing I have to a "Theo-logical" position on this matter is that digging holes right now is a lot more interesting than thinking about what goes into them in the hereafter.

So if humans think that being buried alongside their dog is a good idea then they should contact their representative. But don't expect any lobbying from us.

And just for the legislative record, if it turns out there is such a thing as reincarnation, I'd like to come back as a dog.

JOURNEY

I don't exactly have the literary pedigree to back this up, (although I do have a BOW (bachelor's of woofology degree, honorary of course) but I suspect that whomever said the journey is in the *going* not the *getting* there was very likely a dog.

Of course the Internet says differently, crediting the sentiment to everyone from Heraclitus to Ernest Hemingway but the Internet also has some interesting opinions on UFOs and ghosts.

And far greater literary minds than mine are still arguing about who really wrote Shakespeare's sonnets. My suggestion, cherchez le chien.

But all that is for future symposia (try the cheese cubes, I say, they're tasty) the point is that for a dog everything is a journey and (with the possible exception of the kennel, and the vet) we don't care much where we go. A trip to the park is terrific of course, but we're just as excited to get milk, walk to the mailbox, drop off the dry cleaning or pay an overdue library fine.

Count us in, we say.

Every time.

A dog would never say you can't get there from here (sounds suspiciously cat-like) More likely if we were so philosophically inclined (we seldom are), he'd say there's no there, only over here, and over here. Let's check it out. Or as J.R.R. Tolkien('s dog) put it, "Not all those who wander are lost."

In fact, we're seldom lost, although our owners often think we are. We prefer to think of it as "on assignment," and if that assignment takes us deep into the woods, or out of sight, or off chasing squirrels then so be it.

Most of the time when our owners are reduced to nervously shouting our names (repeating yourself doesn't really help) while we're exploring a steam, they're the ones who are lost and we mostly come back in due time to soothe their nerves. Of course, they could try following their noses.

Good luck on that one.

My master, for example could get lost going into the next room. And put him into a strange city... forget about it. In fact, the only bad thing about going for ride with my two masters is listening to them fight over directions.

"Let's turn left says one, we've been making a lot of rights." Or "did the gas station attendant say turn at the first Dunkin Donuts, or the second?"

Get a GPS, I say. Or listen to your dog.

The nice thing about not caring much where you're going is that you are seldom disappointed with your destination. Just get the car going and roll down the window, we say. The road will provide.

Of course someone has to know where we're going. Someone has to pick up the kids at ballet practice, car pool to school, buy the groceries, and go to work. Someone can't really afford to just put his head out the window to feel the wind in his face because someone has to prevent the car from crashing into a tree.

I'm just glad that *someone* isn't me.

That's why whenever dogs get into the car, they seldom want to drive.

The passenger seat suits us just fine.

LoST

A dog's life is full of human words and phrases that seem to trip off the tongue but which really leave us scratching our heads (not that there's anything wrong with that.) For example when a human says "soon," we think he means "now". When he says "later" we think he means "now." And when he says "walk" we are absolutely certain that what we've just heard is "now, now now."

By my master's count (another thing I can't do and don't miss), I have only about 25 words and 23 of them are "now" with the other two being "walk," and "dinner."

It has been said by those who keep track of such things that Eskimos have 100 words for snow which a Siberian Husky of my acquaintance tells me really isn't that surprising considering how often it snows and how little else Eskimos apparently have to talk about. I mean if people kept asking you how was the weather in a place where all it does is snow, you might come up with 100 different ways to keep up the conversation just to be polite.

I am ever polite and find that my considerable charm is not at all diminished (and in fact enhanced) by keeping my mouth shut. My limited vocabulary seems quite sufficient for my simple needs despite my master's insistence that I learn some new words every so often. I look at these efforts in the same way I consider his desire to play fetch -- a game which I've always thought pointless even though I am a retriever. Still, considering that he is in charge of dinner (now there's a word I know) I humor him by running back and forth until one of us is exhausted, which is nearly always him.

I've heard that somewhere there is a border collie who has over 1,000 words in his vocabulary, which must make him appear quite smart to humans but doesn't impress me one bit. I figure that if I had 1,000 words 998 would turn out to be "now" and alert readers who can maintain focus for

more than three paragraphs (now there's a trick) could guess the other two. And as for the chatty Kathy border collie whose brobdignagian vocabulary seems to only earn him further experimentation, I propose a more practical test -- put both of us together at meal time and see who gets to the bottom of the supper bowl first, and who goes home hungry after reciting the Gettysburg Address.

All of which I suppose is good fodder (not that there's anything wrong with that) for dog linguists who seem intent on showing how smart they are by showing how smart we are, but I say better to let sleeping dogs lie instead of making them talk, which like trying to teach a pig to sing is generally a waste of time for both teacher and pig.

The point is that a big vocabulary is not all it's cracked up to be and it is very often the case that the more words you have the more trouble you can find yourself in.

Like all mothers everywhere, my mother always said that if you can't say something nice about someone then don't say anything, which is pretty obvious for a species that doesn't confuse talking with intelligence but which judging from recent human presidential debates seems pretty much beyond the understanding of most two-legged folk, their mothers notwithstanding.

Which I suppose is why you are unlikely to catch a dog running for president and speechifying on the rubber chicken circuit.

Not that there's anything wrong with running of course, but frankly, we much prefer the rubber chicken.

If it were up to us, English would have about 10 words and three of them would be variations of "eat." Give us two more to mean "walk," one to mean "out" and there would be four left over just in case any of us decided to write the great canine novel.

The rest of human discourse goes pretty much over our heads, and beneath our notice, which works out fine for all concerned except for the two human words which we consider the saddest ever uttered.

One of the best things about being a dog is that our default setting is happy.

This is what allows us to greet our human companions each day as if they had just returned home from the 100 years war and at the same time be absolutely ecstatic that they are serving us the same old dog food for dinner.

We seldom suffer from unrequited love as we love (and are loved) by just about everyone and our limited memory means it is just about impossible for us to hold a grudge. Because we live in the present we are unworried about the future and we have a simple answer to those reincarnationists who would ask us how we would like to return in some other life.

Why, as a dog of course.

We remain unfazed by the endless amount of chatter from the humans that surround us who even after centuries of being in charge seem to be able to come up with endless ways of saying that they are not happy, blah,blah, blah.

Still, there are two human words which give pause (not that there is anything wrong with paws) to even the happiest of dogs.

"Lost dog."

We see these words on posters nailed to trees, on supermarket bulletin boards, and in the waiting room of veterinarians. In the digital age, they appear online at such sites as lostmydoggie.com where an endless parade of sad tales await of Sophie, Tucker, Lucky (apparently misnamed) from Tennessee, New Mexico, and right around the block, all looking teary-eyed and decidedly undoglike.

Because they are lost.

And thank goodness, mostly found. If lostmydoggie.com can be believed, it turns out that with the help of the Internet, most of the lost animals find their way home either by their own wits or through the kindness of strangers, appearing a few hours or days later as the proverb says "wagging their tails behind them" which when you think about it is the only place a tail can reasonably wag from.

Still, I worry for all those lost dogs and their heartbroken masters because even a few moments of being lost is sadder than most dogs and their companions can imagine.

I am seldom lost, but occasionally out of sight as I explore the woods while my master contents himself to follow the trails of those who have set out before him. Occasionally I hear him repeatedly shouting my name (as if I don't hear him the first time) before I amble from behind the trees to the great relief of all concerned. And even though it has been only a few minutes, I always knew where he was so it was technically him and not me who was lost; by the look on his face I have learned one thing.

Now I know what it feels like to be greeted as if I had just come back from the 100 years war.

PHOTO

So here we are sitting on the porch drinking iced tea (actually the guests are drinking the tea, I prefer water fresh from a stream), ooh and ahhing over pictures of me and, frankly, I'm confused.

Now considering my acknowledged problem with short term memory, you might think being confused is a common circumstance for me, but that's not really the case.

Sure, I may have trouble remembering where I was an hour ago, but I know where I am now and usually that's enough. I can remember where my house is and the park, and when it's time for dinner. Remembering stuff beyond that, like old grudges and being left out of family weddings is more trouble than it's worth. I don't often give humans advice (not that they don't need it), but here comes some: Why remember something if it just makes you mad?

But I do remember being confused on that summer night on the porch because everyone was staring at the photos of me, but I WAS RIGHT THERE.

Go figure.

Not that I should have been surprised by the human fascination with photographs; our house is lousy with them. You can't go into a room and not see a picture of one of the children even though it wasn't that long ago that all of them lived here.

And people think I have a problem with a short term memory?

And those are just the photos on the wall. Add to them the hundreds gathering dust in shoeboxes, which are mostly good for chewing (the box or the photos, it depends on my mood), and the thousands taking up pixel space on the hard drive and we're practically drowning in images.

And what's the point? So that guests can look right past me and at my photo and remark how beautiful I am?

Here's a thought. Try petting me.

Maybe it's just me but still photos have always left me cold largely because they're so, well, still.

And I seldom am. If you subtract the time I'm sleeping (which admittedly is a lot) then I'm just about always in motion.

Take a still photo of me running in the woods and what you have captured is fundamentally unreal. Sure, photos have the ability to freeze action, but think where that could lead. I suppose that if there were a camera that could freeze a squirrel long enough for me to catch it, I might be interested. But how long before some squirrel lover would just turn around and freeze me? Sounds cold, and not really sporting.

Even moving photos don't capture the real me. If you want to see how I look as I bound through the snow, put down your camera and put on your boots. Then follow me.

So no thanks. I know I'm slobbering in the wind here, but I think I speak for all dogs when I say we could do with fewer photos of us rather than more.

I suppose all those photos are OK for celebrity dogs and their puppyrazzi, and I guess they help sell calendars and coffee mugs (although we never get the royalties) but if you want to really know us, try taking us for a walk, or a swim, or a drive with our heads hanging out the back window.

Try remembering us for how we are right now instead of trying to freeze us and squeeze us in a camera frame.

And never ever ask us to smile.

CAMERA SHY

For someone who hears on a regular basis how beautiful he is (it's really not as tiresome as it sounds) I am surprisingly camera shy.

And although I have more than once been called a "walking photo opportunity," I am quite happy to pass up the opportunity and just take the walk.

There is just something about standing in front of camera that doesn't quite click (a camera metaphor now out of date since most human photo buffs prefer to catch me via instagram).

Still, it is quite common for seeming strangers to stop me on the street to ask if they can take a picture of me. Of course I am too polite to refuse (I can't really claim credit, it's my breeding) but really what's the point?

I am, after all, me, and not a picture of me. To pretend otherwise seems artificial and entirely undoglike.

Generally such photo seekers will first ask that I cease what I am doing be it hole digging, stick chewing or ball chasing; all of which are infinitely more interesting than staring in the direction of the person who has interrupted me from these far more exciting canine pursuits.

No wonder the whole endeavor makes me somewhat squirrelly (not that's there anything wrong with squirrels except their annoying habit of high tailing -- ditto nothing wrong with high tails - at the sight of me.)

Yet humans persist, asking me first to look into the camera and say "cheese," which I mistakenly mistake as an offer of food, but which they mean to be "smile," whatever that is, although it appears to have something to do with baring my teeth something a dog of my upbringing would never do under any circumstances.

And so the entire picture taking moment turns out to be something of a muddle (nothing wrong with mud) with the photographer jumping about trying to get me to stand still as I jump about trying to get away, all as he

repeats the silly request to show my teeth which despite my good breeding I am sorely tempted to do.

Candidly, he should try candidly, by which I mean stop posing and try catching up to me as I run, play, fetch or chase and then exactly when I'm not looking -- that's the time to take my picture.

Snap.

I suppose photographs do have some lasting value that are not immediately apparent to one who lives entirely in the present. And I suppose that if a photographer captured enough images of me at various times and various seasons in my life then I just might be interested in seeing a scrapbook of me being me through the years.

Of course to create such a photo scrapbook I'd need paper, glue, scissors , and not least of all an opposable thumb.

But I'm not worried.

I have a human for that.

WHERE THE
WILD THINGS ARE

FoxES

From the researchers with too much time on their hands department comes a recent study from the University of Illinois where investigators claim they were able to breed a strain of foxes that were – get this -- as friendly as your average golden retriever.

Foxes? Seriously?

Now as a far above average golden retriever, far be it from me to malign any fellow creature (human researchers are a different story) but I've met one or two foxes in my travels and friendliness is not exactly the description that comes to mind.

About the best I can say is that your average fox ranks slightly ahead of racoons on the glad-to-meet-you scale but that is faint praise indeed for a species that most canines of my acquaintance know to approach with a good degree of caution.

Not to mention the long-held wisdom of hens in henhouses who know that encountering one in residence is hardly the occasion for breaking out the good china.

In fact it is common knowledge in the animal kingdom that foxes should be approached with caution reserved for porcupines and skunks and with the wisdom that such encounters generally end badly.

Humans seem to know this instinctively (and they have notoriously poor instincts) as you seldom see foxes at playgrounds, ball fields where dogs are routinely and (for the most part) enthusiastically welcomed to add to the general festive spirt and bonhomie that has been their trademark since the first wolves gave up traveling packs and decided that dinner could be more efficiently and reliably delivered by humans out of a supper bowl.

Such is hardly the case for your average fox who tends to be an unmannerly guest at human gatherings and could not be relied upon to fetch a ball, catch a frisbee or good naturedly accept petting from small children and would more likely (and more properly) be considered a cause for alarm despite any assurances from white coated researchers who might not know the difference between a fox and fox terrier.

It all brings to mind a fable (a genre in which foxes appear frequently, though rarely for their friendliness.)

A scorpion in need of a ride across a river promises to not sting a turtle in return for safe passage on the turtle's back. Midway across, the scorpion stings the turtle sending both to a watery doom. As the turtle expires he asks why the scorpion would do such a thing as now they would both die.

"It's my nature," the scorpion replied.

As they attempt to engineer the nature of foxes, Illinois researchers would do well to consider the tale of the scorpion before spending their time trying to create a fox as friendly as a golden retriever.

Let foxes be foxes I say, and if you want an animal as friendly as a golden retriever then my unscientific advice is that you go out and get one.

SQUIRRELS

"Ah, but a man's reach should exceed his grasp, or what's a heaven for?" - Robert Browning.

I've never met Robert Browning but he seems like a thoughtful dog. Nice coloring, I presume.

Anyway I agree with his sentiments as my reach often exceeds my grasp. Just try leaving an apple pie too close to the counter and you'll see what I mean. Same with cannolis (my favorite), oatmeal cookies, baseball caps, stray socks, or that doggie toy you meant to surprise me with later.

This especially applies to anything that falls to the ground, which I consider my home field. Once it hits the floor, it's up for grabs, and I always grab. And if it needs a tiny nudge to the floor, say from off the edge of a coffee table, then who am I to say no.

And I never say no.

But it's not until we head out into the woods that the true wisdom of dog Browning's words sets in.

I mean squirrels.

Now I know that some people think that the natural antagonists to dogs are cats, but this isn't quite true. I know plenty of households where cats and dogs live quite harmoniously and while I don't have many cat friends they certainly don't run away the minute I approach. Humans tend to pair us together, saying things like they fight like cats and dogs, when mostly we're a live and let live bunch. And some of the things they say about us make no sense at all. I've heard some humans say it's raining cats and dogs but I've been out in the rain plenty of times and never once been struck by any four-legged creatures let alone falling canines or felines. That sounds very dangerous on both ends of the rainstorm if you ask me.

The best I can say about cats is that they seem to have their own agenda which make them appear to be self-involved, but which really might mean that they're just not into me that much. And while I find that astounding, I can live with it.

Raccoons are a different story. They're just mean old coots. They never seem happy to see you; just about insist that you get out of their way; have an unnatural attraction to trash and always look like they're up to no good.

I think that's why they were born with masks.

But back to squirrels. They're not cautious like cats, or mean like raccoons. I've seen deer that are afraid of their shadows who were happier to see me. The only thing I can say about them is that they are squirrelly, which you wouldn't even think is a human word but if you go to the dictionary, there it is.

Squirrelly.

The truth is I can't even tell if I like squirrels because I've never really met one. It's certainly not for lack of trying. Put me, or any self-respecting dog into the woods for five minutes and give us the scent of a squirrel and we're off, bounding through the high grass and jumping over logs trying to make their acquaintance. And what do they do?

They run. Up trees, over branches, and through meadows in the kind of down and out patterns that any NFL running back would die for. I've even seen a few run out into moving traffic just to avoid me and you know how dangerous that can be.

And why? What did I or some long ago ancestor do to squirrels that makes them head for the hills the minute I come their way? Did I eat their family? (please, I do just fine on table scraps) Did I take their homes? (who would want to live in a tree; heights make me nervous) Did I steal their food? (acorns make me gag.)

And yet they run and I chase, and they run, and I chase. It seems so pointless. The pathetic part is I know that even if I caught one, it would probably be so sick and aged that we could never have a meaningful relationship. And as for catching up to a healthy squirrel long enough to make his acquaintance, I may as well try to catch a cats-and-dog raindrop.

Still like Browning dog, I'll keep trying because a dog's reach should always exceed its grasp.

And if I ever get to doggie heaven I hope it will be chock full of pleased-to-meet-you squirrels.

OWLS

It's something of a canine fact of life that wherever we go, we turn heads.

Ever since I was a pup it was painfully obvious to my master that whenever a passersby encountered us on our morning constitutional and apropos of nothing blurted out "you're beautiful," they never ever meant him.

Not that it fazes me of course. In fact, it is quite easy to get used to being the center of attention, a fact even more apparent once I added my local celebrity role as the nation's only regularly appearing canine columnist.

So imagine my surprise when on a recent walk through our city's Forest Park I came upon a gathering of humans toting binoculars, telescopes and long distance lenses intent upon gazing not at me, who would have been quite apparent to the naked eye, but at a rather muddled spot of gray 50 feet straight up in the trees.

At a nest of great horned owls.

Now I've got nothing against owls, except perhaps their reputation among humans for wisdom which I must say among the canine set is considered largely undeserved.

I mean I've never seen an owl sit on command, or fetch, or do any of the many behaviors which even the most unwise dogs can do in return for a treat and the universal praise we all long for – good dog.

I've never heard anyone utter "good owl," making all the more curious any claim to greatness; frankly I've seen better horns on several fawns of my acquaintance. In fact, I saw little going on in their nest that rose above the merely interesting, and even that would be a stretch (not that there's anything wrong with stretching) unless you happened to be another owl.

And yet the humans below seemed absolutely enthralled by the pretty much nothing that was happening high in the trees, elbowing each other out of the way to catch a glimpse of even the slightest movement in the nest and scanning the nearby trees for any sign of mama and papa owl.

Seriously?

Naturally I ambled over in the gawker's direction to see what the hub-bub was about, fully expecting the assembled birdwatchers to immediately drop their binoculars in favor of the infinitely more interesting goings-on at ground level.

And yet there they stood, eyes fixed skyward, pausing only to suggest to each other perhaps a better angle through the trees and utterly oblivious to the charm magnet that was standing right before them.

Me.

No good dog, no beautiful dog, no "can I pet the dog." Please.

Nothing. Astonishing.

Not that I didn't try my usual tricks. I rolled over, I nuzzled, I even tried chasing my tail. In short, I gave them the full-blown cuteness assault. Frank-ly, I would have settled for a few pats on the head and the perfunctory "good dog" and been on my way, but there was nothing I could do to budge those owl watchers from well, watching.

Of course I'm not jealous; OK, a bit; you bet.

But I'm not worried. In a few weeks those baby owls will have left the nest, mom and pop owl will have flown off to parts unknown and I'll be back to being top dog.

And you know whoooo will be king of the park again.

Ticks

"I hate ticks."

There, I've said it.

And while it might not be politically correct (insect lovers, spare me your letters) fortunately, the tick lobby is small.

I'm sure that ticks, like everything have their place in the grand scheme but should I arrive in the great beyond one day and be granted one question to the maker of all things I intend to ask, "why ticks?"

I'm sure it's been asked before.

Ticks enjoy a special place in the hateful firmament.

It's not like I hate squirrels, although I futilely chase them every chance I get. I guess you could say I hate squirrels in the way rival sports teams hate each other. What they really hate is losing; the rest is really respect.

But how can anyone respect ticks whose lot in life seems to be to lie in wait like roadside brigands for unwary passersby and then to literally suck their blood often leaving behind microorganisms that can cause a lifetime of pain.

They use their eight legs (I don't trust an animal with more than four, with the possible exception of an octopus whom I have yet to encounter) not for cavorting or exploring as any dog would, but to dig deep into skin and hold on for dear life while they engorge themselves (gentle readers might wish to turn away here) for hours, getting ever larger in a display of bloodsucking that would make a vampire blush.

About the only good thing that can be said of ticks is that, unlike vampires, they don't live very long. Often the object of germ warfare and a media campaign showing them mercilessly attacked by microscopic commandos, they are given no quarter once discovered by humans where they are (justly I may add) tweezed away, or burned out and sent to a watery grave down the toilet bowl.

And should they survive all this, Nature takes over, killing them off each winter at the first frost and seemingly ending the scourge forever.

And yet, not.

Scientists say that despite the cold winter, this is expected to be a banner year for ticks, which is good news if you're an eight-legged blood sucker but is unlikely to kick off any parades in the canine community.

For us it means that there will be more and more of the little buggers this summer lurking along the byways of the forest and hiding in the high grass of the meadow waiting to pounce and subjecting yet new generations of woodland creatures to their devilish credo:

I suck, therefore I am.

What's a dog to do? Ticks can't be scared off like squirrels or chipmunks; they're too small to eat; and they can't be reasoned with (how do you talk to what is essentially a pair of jaws?) I suppose they could be avoided if one were willing to stay inside all summer, but what self-respecting dog would do that? Humans can wear long pants and high socks but canines generally eschew such fashion and frankly we would look downright silly among our sylvan peers who in general like to go au natural.

About the only thing that can be done with ticks is to suffer them, enduring only modestly effective anti-tick treatments monthly and then relying on the kindness of our masters to inspect us after summer outings and give our unwelcome hitchhikers their just deserts.

I suppose I should feel some compassion for a species that will never be called man's (or any creature's) best friend. After all, no one ever asked to be born a tick? And if there is any truth to this reincarnation business (I believe I was president of the United States before I evolved into a Golden retriever) then I might come back as a tick in which case I suppose I'd have some explaining to do.

I suppose the most charitable thing to do is to just accept the presence of ticks in about the same way one might accept earthquakes, or tidal waves, as a part of a grand design too complicated for animals of my pay grade to understand.

But I'd rather just hate them.

There, I've said it again

SKUNKS

If dogs had a philosophy (other than Descartes' dog – I nap therefore I am), it would be live and let live.

For the most part we recognize that we are all God's creatures (except for the mean mongrel down the street who apparently did not get the memo) and few of us have a mean bone (not that there's anything wrong with bones... yum) in our bodies.

Even when we chase squirrels, we do it more out of curiosity than malevolence and if I were ever to catch one (full disclosure – it hasn't happened yet) I suspect my first words to him would be not "prepare to die" but more likely "how do you do?"

And I freely admit that I would (and do) make a poor watchdog as my entire emphasis would be on watching, which I could probably do for hours as nefarious humans emptied the house.

None of which prepared me for my recent encounter with a certain striped and suspiciously named Mephitis mephitis (would any scientist name me Theo, Theo?) more commonly known as the common skunk who I happened to bump into during a late-night stroll in my backyard. And while the Internet calls skunks (and I am not making this up) "intelligent and affectionate creatures that are quickly becoming popular family pet choices," I believe my place in the house as pet is secure which is more than I can say for the skunk who showed his intelligence and affection by leaving me an odoriferous souvenir of our meeting and slipping off into the night.

Not that I really minded. We dogs have a keen sense of smell and strong odors are more likely considered a treat than a trick. When I return fresh from the forest where I have been dashing through mud and rolling around in all kinds of unmentionables only to be reminded that I smell "like a dog," I consider it a compliment. And when I take such compliments -- as I do all compliments -- to mean come closer for petting I am astonished at the common human reaction which is to hold one's nose (theirs, not mine, -- whomever it was who said the nose, "knows" was certainly not speaking of human noses). Just what did humans expect from my skunking? That I would smell like a flower? Just what is it that the human nose thinks it knows? And what animal in its right mind would hold its nose, even if such a thing were possible?

But back to the skunk, who I bore no ill will (remember my philosophy) even though our interaction had suddenly made me canine non gratis around the house.

After all, I wasn't injured; perhaps he was trying to be friendly? And from the skunk's point of view (a perspective seldom taken by humans) maybe the smell was not so bad. Lots of things that smell perfectly awful to humans smell just dandy to dogs (I know a few who eat poop.) In the end, he was mostly a skunk being a skunk and what fair-minded animal can really argue with that?

Yet I must say that the humans around the house seemed to view my skunking quite differently, occasioning a brisk discussion from a distance about the merits of tomato juice and other home remedies most of which turned out to be old wives tales (not that there's anything wrong with old wives who generally turn out to be just fine dog owners.) After another visit to the Internet (why would anyone return to a source that had just pronounced skunks "affectionate"?) it was agreed to try a mixture of hydrogen peroxide, baking soda and dishwashing liquid which to my mind was barely an improvement over skunk smell but seemed to work fine according to the human nose, which any dog can tell you is far inferior to the canine variety.

Several applications later I was deemed "cured" of my skunking and allowed to return to the house with the stern warning to stay away from skunks, which considering all the kafuffle seemed like a sensible idea, although difficult to put into practice.

But I get it. Humans don't like skunks and if I intend to spend my life with humans I may as well get used to their prejudices.

It's either that or running off and living with the skunks and I doubt that they would be as reliable at calling me a "good dog" most of the day and filling my dish at dinnertime.

SMART

Lately, I've noticed a growing cottage industry (not that there's anything wrong with cottages –some of my best friends live in the them) of human scientists making a pretty good living spending years doing experiments the results of which any dog could tell you if anyone had just asked.

Namely, that dogs are smarter than cats.

If humans were so smart, you would have thought they would have guessed that. But don't take my word for it even though I don't really know how to lie (that seems to be a human thing.)

Instead take the word of Suzana Herculano-Houzel of Vanderbilt University who set out to study the number of neurons in the brains of animals proving conclusively to my way of thinking that humans have too much time on their hands.

Anyway, after examining the brains of a variety of cats, ferrets, mongooses (or is that mongeese) raccoons, lions and -- get this-- golden retrievers (I'm afraid to ask how) she reported her completely unstartling conclusion that: a) dogs were smarter than cats and, b) that golden retrievers were smarter than striped hyenas.

And while I have no idea of what to make of that second finding (I've never actually engaged in dinner conversation with a striped hyena) the first conclusion seems so obvious that I am sure your average striped hyena would have no trouble believing it.

Ms. Herculano-Houzel, who burnished her impressive academic credentials by admitting that she is an avowed dog lover, backed up her findings by reporting quite scientifically that dogs have 530 million neurons in the cerebral cortex of their brains while cats have only half that amount.

Neurons for the striped hyenas in the crowd, are the information-processing units in the brain, and the cerebral cortex is the part of the brain that can combine information from different sources and create new associations, recognize patterns, make decisions to act differently based on past experience and start making predictions for the future.

Which means (and remember this is Herculano-Houzel talking, so cat lovers can send their letters to her) dogs can be expected to be capable of more complex and flexible behavior such as guard work, movie acting, first responding and assisting the blind, while cats can be counted on to well, use a litter box.

Now cat lovers will undoubtedly say that cats could do any of those things if they so desired but just don't want to give their human masters the satisfaction. All of this may be true (although my 530 million neurons have never been enough for me to figure out cats) I still can't see why delivering satisfaction should be considered a bad thing.

By way of reference, Herculano-Houzel did point out that humans possess roughly 16 billion cortical neurons so that we canines are in no danger of taking over governance of the planet anytime soon; which suits me fine.

But considering the mess that humans have been making of things lately, frankly if given a choice, I'd vote for the striped hyena.

LOVE CATS

In a special delivery from the "everybody knows that" department comes the wholly unstartling scientific study that shows dogs really do love you more than cats.

Five times more to be exact according to researchers who analyzed saliva from dogs and cats after playing with their owners for 10 minutes (I'm amazed they could get a cat to play for 10 minutes without the cat getting bored and retreating under a couch) and learned that the hormone connected to love and bonding jumped nearly 60 percent for the dogs and a paltry 12 percent for cats.

Ho-hum which is about the reaction cats give to most everything, or as a teen-age dog of my acquaintance would say "duh." And while I generally disapprove of such canine slang (what's the point of being able to talk if you don't use your words) I must say that in this one case he has put his thumb (if he had a thumb) on the matter.

Now I'm all in favor of scientific research if it comes up with a better mousetrap (not that there's anything wrong with mice) or a better tick collar (the one exception to my general live and let live philosophy toward the animal kingdom.) But in this case I could have saved the scientific community years of study by just inviting the researchers to leave the lab and come to my home for supper where they would witness the universal canine greeting which could best be described as if everyone had just returned from the 100 years war.

Try the same test at any cat's home and the response would have been one of indifference mixed with annoyance that the 100 years war had taken so long resulting in the great inconvenience toward the 100 years of cats waiting for dinner.

Or to put it another way, were Disney productions ever to make a movie to be called "cat-sa-blanca," (an ill-advised move in my opinion) dogs would be the Humphrey Bogart character waiting wide-eyed at the train station in the pouring rain while cats are sitting out the war in the company of some guy named Sam playing with yarn endlessly again and again while remarking that you'll always have Paris, or Rome, or Schenectady, or whatever.

In a way it's comforting to know that the lack of feline affection isn't personal; like everything else we think is love it's just hormones. No amount of petting, purring or springing for the gourmet cat food is likely to arouse much more than a nod from a species who if the roles were reversed and they were in charge would very likely be eyeing you for dinner.

It's the oxytocin, that same hormone that floods through moms at the first sight of their newborns and which somehow is in scarce supply at the sound of the words here, kitty, kitty. In fact, the one of the somewhat dog-biased researchers said he was quite surprised to learn that cats produce any oxytocin at all.

Now none of this means that cat owners don't love their cats. Romeo may love Juliet, but don't expect her cat to be much impressed by either of them. In the end, saliva tells all and what it's telling is the same thing that dogs and dog owners have known since the first wolf decided that loving one master was a lot better than hunting in packs.

Humans may love their cats, but frankly, cats just don't give a spit.

CAT IN THE HAT

Maybe it's just a species thing, or too much time watching Tom and Jerry cartoons as a pup, but I generally don't have much good to say about cats.

It's not that I hate cats. After all, we are all God's creatures and if the creator of all things saw fit to create cats then he must have had a good reason other than sheer orneriness. And I must say that even the most ornery of felines still ranks above ticks (they make my skin crawl); raccoons (I've never seen one back down from a fight) and owls (I have a recurring nightmare that one will swoop down and carry me away in the night).

But that's just me, and I recognize that ranking cats above insects, night prowlers and irrational fears is faint praise indeed. But the thing about cats is that I just can't figure them out. One minute they're giving you this come hither look and the next you're scratching bits of their claws out of your fur.

Of course all this applies only to actual cats. Fictional ones I like just fine and perhaps none more than our own native son feline, the Cat in the Hat.

Part of my admiration for the cantankerous fellow comes from our strong neighborhood ties. Full disclosure, I have grown up just down the block from the boyhood home of his creator Theodor Geisel's on Fairfield Street. In fact, a bit of human research (dogs are oddly uncurious about family history) shows that the house in which I now reside was occupied many dog years ago by young Ted's grandmother and that Ted himself has been said to have a long-time affinity for the hills and dales of the very Forest Park that are now my stomping grounds.

And so naturally I am glad to embrace my Seussian roots along with his most famous creation, the Cat in the Hat, who took center stage a few weeks ago as the city of Springfield formally opened its Seuss museum a hop skip and dog jump away at the city's Quadrangle. The opening was much heralded by a formal reception (no dogs or cats for that matter allowed) and

a much more pet friendly parade led by a several stories-tall Cat in the Hat balloon accompanied by school children, politicians of all stripes (I love stripes) and assorted local notables down Mulberry Street, up Maple and onto the new museum grounds.

It's almost enough to make me rethink my position about cats.

Of course wherever the cat was thing one and thing two were never far behind along with the entire menagerie of the Seuss imagination that has kept children enthralled for generations. In later years Dr. Seuss developed a more philosophical bent taking on racism, big government and promising generations of college graduates of the many places they'll go as they emerge into adulthood.

Maybe it's because I'm a simple dog myself, or maybe it's because I'll never get to graduate from anything more than dog obedience school, but I keep coming back to that mischievous cat and his completely false promise that lives deep in the heart of all children that any mess can be fixed before mom gets home. It's not true of course but still it's a nice thought.

And just the sort of thing I wish I had thought of first. It's not that I'm jealous. OK, maybe a little. You bet. Perhaps there is still room for a dog on a log, or a fish in a dish, or a horse on a golf course.

I think I'll put my agent right on it.

UNCLE

Congratulations are in order.

Of course when you're a dog, congratulations are always in order, which probably explains why we so seldom get them.

I mean a dog's life is pretty good. I suppose we could be congratulated for being lovable, or loyal, or romping through the woods, or chasing squirrels, or for not being born a vole, or for just being so darn cute, but really what would be the point?

In the end, it would come down to "Congratulations, you're a dog."

Still, in this case congratulations are definitely called for.

Because today, I'm an uncle.

Now technically, I was born an uncle. Although I was named after Theo Epstein, the then-general manager of the Boston Red Sox, I have been reliably told since that my name in Greek means "Uncle," which means that I've always been an uncle.

And now I'm an uncle uncle.

The reason for my uncle uncle status (or maybe it's second uncle once removed, who can be sure?) is that my master's daughter has acquired her first dog, a Vizsla named Mango. And while I must say that the breed sounds like a foreign car (frankly, I don't understand why anyone would want anything other than a golden retriever, specifically, me), I like to consider all animals (with the possible exception of ticks) as God's creatures and therefore deserving of a hearty doggy welcome.

Prejudice does not become us.

And so when I heard that my master's daughter had acquired a dog for her household, I naturally reveled in my new role as uncle uncle and shared in her feelings that a long-standing wrong had now been righted.

As readers may recall, my master always resisted bringing a dog into the household as long as his children lived there for the unstated but obvious reason that three daughters were quite enough to manage without an additional four legs under foot.

And he remained immune to their importunings and bald lies that: a) having a dog would calm things down and, b) that such a hypothetical dog would be no trouble as said daughters would take charge of its care and feeding.

Which often led to long and messy dog fights that I was just as happy to miss, and concluded with the vow - especially from the eldest - that as soon as she left the house, she would get a dog of her own.

So now she has.

I would certainly have loved to see my dog nephew for myself, but it turns out that my masters chose to make the visit by plane and the airlines take a certain dogist approach to canine travelers, preferring instead to treat their customers like dogs by squeezing them like sardines (not that I have anything against sardines . . . yum) and charging them for everything in sight such as baggage, extra leg room (and I am not making this up) at times, toilet privileges.

Believe me, things will be different if dogs ever start running the airlines as our aim is to constantly please, a goal that left the airline business long ago along with the free peanuts.

But until I get to fly the unfettered skies for myself, I have to make do with reports of the visit with my nephew, which I must say by all accounts were nothing less than glowing.

He was loving, curious, friendly, energetic and in all ways puppylike, which of course is high praise coming from a dog even if such exuberance at times resulted in some chewed up shoelaces, scratched furniture and occasional lapses in paper training - all perfectly excusable I must say.

Judging from his photo, I suspect in no time he will be up and playing in full dog glory, and I look forward to meeting him for some good old-fashioned squirrel chasing and dog-wrastling.

We'll see which one of us is the first to cry "uncle."

VIZSLA

Ninety-nine percent of the time I'm 100 percent happy being exactly who I am.

Unlike humans who seem to wish away much of their lives longing to be taller or slimmer or smarter, or richer (a particularly odd desire since you can't eat money, despite a Jack Terrier of my acquaintance who tried it once and spent the night at the vet's having a fistful of pennies yanked out of his gut), dogs have very little interest in being anything but, well, dogs.

One of the reasons you hear so little about dog genies is that no dog would know what to do if he ever met one. Offer your average dog (although we are all above average) three wishes and he would wish to be a dog. And then he'd wish it again. And again.

Even the thought of being something else leaves me scratching my head (nothing wrong with that.) A cat?-- too complicated. A skunk? Too odorous (although I think they smell fine). A squirrel? – OK, maybe for a minute so I could finally catch myself and see what I was running away from.

Still, there's no doubt that a dog's life is for me. And yet I'm only human (thank goodness it's just an expression.) And if I were ever granted a wish, I just might want to know how it felt to be descended from Hungarian royalty; to be two feet tall, short-haired, toothpick-legged and seemingly all-lung.

In short, I Veesh I Vas a Vizsla.

Alert readers may remember that when my master's daughter was of dog-owning age (her parents denying her repeated requests as a child for a canine companion on the grounds that she had, get this, *sisters*) she surprised all observers (me) by choosing not a golden retriever but a canine marathoner whose singular trait seemed to be the ability to run forever and then collapse into a ball that could not be budged.

In so doing, she forwent the usual torrent of compliments that comes with

retriever ownership and consigned herself to providing long-winded explana-
tions of her new pet's Magyar roots in response to the generally well-meaning
question of passers-by, "what's that?"

Of course she responded politely (it's her breeding) when she could get her
dog to stand still long enough to model but which nevertheless could get tiresome (for her, Vizslas seldom tire) but which left her longing for occasions when
Vizslas could just be Vizslas and hence the longing for a Vizsla meet-up.

Goldens generally have little need for meet-ups. Take a golden to a dog park
and he is just as happy to rub noses with whatever Labradors, terriers and
setters he should meet there. But Vizslas are a rare breed and sometimes feel
the need to be around dogs who are just like them. And since short of putting
together a part-cheetah, part-rabbit and part-reindeer in a laboratory, no dog
is just like them, they and their owners will often go to great lengths to "meet
up," with their fellow Hungarians.

And occasionally, I get to tag along.

Now as you might imagine this is like inviting a football player to a track
meet. And while I've always considered myself an above average cavorter, that
is nothing like trying to keep up with a pack of Vizslas flying down a beach, or
romping through a field and then turning on a dime and doing it at full speed
all over again.

Still, since my general philosophy (as much as a dog can have one) is to never
say no to anything, I always accept an invitation for a Vizsla meet up where I
am generally welcomed into the group in the spirit of a breed that knows what
it's like to be a one of a kind. And I try to keep up with the frantic pace of
being out-run, out-retrieved and generally out-maneuvered which I can usually
do for about 10 minutes after which I am content to amble back to the side-
lines and watch the canine blur that passes before my eyes until I fall asleep.

The outing usually ends with a group picture (trying to get 10 Vizslas into a
picture makes herding cats look like a walk in the park -- nothing wrong with
that) after which I am pronounced an "honorary Vizsla" which I recognize is a
bit like calling an elephant an "honorary" gazelle, but which I take in the spirit
of canine fellowship in which it is offered.

And despite that fleeting one percent of the time of "Vanting to Ve a Vizsla
(actually their accent is not that noticeable, although they do tend to howl a
bit) and imagining what it might be like to run like the wind and then keep on
running, I am happy to return to the 99 percent of my life of semi-celebrity
in which I am pronounced a "good dog," just for hanging around and pretty
much just being me.

COMMUNITY SERVICE

HEALTH PROVIDER

So apparently, now I'm a health provider.

Not a doctor or nurse mind you, positions for which one actually needs training, and how shall I say this - intelligence.

In addition to the opposable thumb thing which I imagine would come in handy when wielding a scalpel, a career in medicine requires a good memory which is not my strong suit. I doubt that I would be able to recall the 206 bones in the human body (and my instinct to regard bones as meant for burying and chewing might be a problem too). And considering my limited life span (I don't like to mention it, but there it is) four years of medical school, plus internship and residency would take up pretty much my whole life, therefore raising the decidedly doglike question, of "what's the point?"

Anyway, when you think about it, doctors and nurses are not really health providers, so much as they are health service providers, who to my way of thinking too often arrive after one is already sick, and the metaphorical horse (or in my case, dog) has left the barn.

I like to think of myself as a true health provider, meaning I can make people healthier just by being, well, me.

And it turns out I am not alone in this opinion.

Here are the facts, courtesy of Glenn Levine, a cardiologist with the Baylor College of Medicine in Houston.

- Dogs may keep owners active (with all those walks). In one study, dog owners were 54 percent more likely than other adults to get recommended levels of exercise.

- Interacting with a pet can lower stress responses in the body.

- Pet ownership is associated with lower blood pressure and cholesterol levels and less obesity.

Now don't ask me how exactly I provide the kind of health benefits you would expect from someone with extensive medical training and princely salary to go along with it.

I keep my master active by taking him along on walks. I suppose he could just take me out to the middle of the woods and leave me there but that has a certain Hansel and Gretel quality to it that does not befit pet ownership. Besides, he might get lost.

I like to think I lower stress by simply exhibiting stress-free behavior. Stress to my way of thinking comes mostly from worry, and I never worry.

It's not like it's a conscious strategy or anything; I just don't do it. You might think there was a tiny bit of anxiety arising from never catching squirrels. But I just wait around for the next squirriel and go after it as if I've been catching them all my life.

No stress; just unjustified and I must say completely illogical hope.

But if the medical evidence says that I lower blood pressure and cholesterol levels in my master with my what-me-worry attitude, who am I to argue?

Mostly I just go about my day. I run hard when there's something to chase, and remain eternally curious about what's around the next bend in the road. I watch my weight by pretty much eating the same thing in the same amount every day (not that I have much choice). And when the going gets tough, I curl up and take a nap.

Then again, perhaps my healing powers come from the fact that I am unflailingly loyal, ever-affectionate and completely nonjudgmental.

You'll never see any of these ingredients in a health food store, or in a doctor's office, but then again they're not the real health providers.

Ask the experts.

I am.

THERAPY

So now, it appears that I am a therapy dog.

Not a "professional" therapist to be sure, which seems to require all sorts of training, certificates, and even internships before being allowed to do what a dog was born to do which is to make people happy.

In fact, I've always thought it was among the great benefits of being a dog that the whole certification process pretty much passes us by. Oh, I suppose if you're a show dog or a police dog or a rescue dog it would be good to have a certain number of bonafides so that humans know you won't run off after the first squirrel you see, but most of the time the main requirement for being a dog is well, being a dog.

Which is what I was being until I noticed that my master didn't seem to be around much. Some careful investigation revealed that he had had his hip replaced (I can relate, golden retrievers have notoriously dodgy hips; it's the price we pay for our swagger) and was recovering at a nearby rehab facility, which I naturally presumed had a no dogs policy because, well, humans are like that.

But lo and behold I was wrong (which proves dog columnists, unlike their human counterparts aren't afraid to admit their mistakes) and in short order I was ready to go (I'm always ready to go) to see if I could cheer him up.

Of course I was well received by my master (he was stuck in bed; where could he go?) but even more surprising was the response of his fellow rehabiltatees who greeted me as if I were visiting royalty and immediately engaged me in conversation about their dogs (living and dead) and how much I reminded them of their happier dog days.

I in turn was happy to hear their stories (sometimes more than once) and embraced my role as in-doggo-parentis; all of which engendered the universal canine compliment that I was a "good dog", an accolade I accepted with my usual aplomb.

Meanwhile up and down the hallway went the news that "there was a dog on the floor" as if I had been dropped from Mars, until I realized that many of the residents didn't get much news and much of it was bad.

Dogs fortunately aren't equipped to give bad news (the worst we can be is a bit of a nuisance around supper time) and we have endless patience. We have the rare ability to never appear bored and I would stack up our emotional intelligence against many overworked and stressed out health professionals.

And we know when to leave, which we sense without insult when all of a sudden people drift off to sleep in our presence.

Fine with me, I say there is always someone else to be visited and a chance to make somebody's day.

Who knows? Some day perhaps I will get officially certified as a dog therapist, but for now I was glad to see my master and spread some doglike cheer along the way.

I sometimes wish humans would take the hint that most of the job in visiting the sick is just to show up. Sometimes you get petted, sometimes you get told to go away. But most of the time you get a chance to make people who feel low feel just a little bit better.

And I can't think of a better job description for a dog than that.

COMFORT

Dogs are not proud by nature.

Oh, we're proud to be dogs all right, as opposed to say, voles or sea slugs. (Please, no letters from the slug lobby. I'm sure your parents love you.)

And we carry ourselves proudly, by which I mean with good posture, which comes mostly from maternal nagging and which I'm counting on to come in handy someday when I spot a squirrel who just might faint away at the sheer majesty of my stature, since, frankly, I don't see any other way I'll ever catch one.

But there's a natural limit to how much we can be proud of our accomplishments because besides bringing joy to the world, we don't actually do much. It's that opposable thumb thing again, coupled with a certain problem with long-term memory that polite dogs generally don't bring up because we actually like hearing the same stories over and over.

Mostly, we go where our owners take us, which is why I was especially proud to see a group of owners from the Lutheran Church Charities in Illinois truck ten of us on a 800-mile road trip to Newtown, Conn., where we tried our best to console anyone who was grieving from the terrible loss of life there, which, of course, happened to be everyone.

The nice thing about dogs and road trips is that you never have to ask twice. And no one had to tell us what to do when we got there, which was just to be ourselves.

We were ourselves at the funerals, we were ourselves on the streets, we were ourselves in the shops and at church. When people wanted to talk, we listened. When they wanted to pray we listened. When they wanted to cry, we snuggled up and then we listened some more.

"Dogs are non-judgmental. They are loving. They are accepting of anyone," said organization president Tim Hetzner, in a pretty good paraphrase of the canine code. "It creates the atmosphere for people to share."

One of the dog handlers called us a natural bridge from sadness to comfort.

We've certainly been called worse, especially when we slobber. It's hard to pinpoint just what it is about us that seems to bring such comfort to humans. Maybe it's that since we can't talk, we really listen. Then again, maybe it's because we're so darn cute.

For dogs, extending comfort is as natural as a walk in the woods. Thank goodness, I've never been called upon to offer comfort under such tragic circumstances, but in my own corner of the world, I've comforted friends, family members, and once, when my master fell in the snow while we were walking, I refused to leave his side until I knew he was all right. True, it's not exactly Lassie and the silver mine stuff, but you don't have to save the world all at once to make it a little better bit by bit. Sadness comes in all sizes, and in the end, so does comfort.

And even if the pain isn't the sort of thing that can be cured by a warm nose, at least dogs know it will never be for lack of trying.

The comfort dog initiative first started in 2008 at Northern Illinois University after a gunman killed five students. A group of dog caretakers associated with Lutheran Church Charities trekked to campus in hopes of providing a distraction to the student community. When not responding to a national tragedy, the Illinois retrievers will often visit people in hospitals, nursing homes and parks. Each dog carries a business card with its name, Facebook page, twitter account and email so those that meet the canine can keep in touch.

Dogs with business cards, doing good. Now that's enough to make any dog proud.

Not of us. Of you.

Take comfort; hug a dog.

FRIENDS AND RELATIONS

BABY

We had a baby visit the house last weekend and frankly I don't understand all the fuss.

Not that I'm unacquainted with fuss; in fact I expect it. It's just that most of the time, the fuss is about me.

"Good dog; you're a good dog; who's the good dog; you're the good dog." A bit repetitive I agree, and probably illustrative of the general tenor of conversation that goes on around the house, but I lap it up (no surprise there; I lap everything up).

I guess I just kind of figured that if you wanted something that was twice as good as a dog, you'd just get two dogs. So imagine my surprise to find that the appearance of a chihuahua-sized bit of humanity could upstage me so completely (whoever said entertainers should never work with dogs or babies should have reminded the dog not to work with the baby.) And to add salt to the wound (not there's anything wrong with salt, yum) the baby was not only greeted as an interesting oddity (I could live with that) but was immediately dubbed by one and all -- get this -- a "good baby."

"Good baby," echoed through the room. Now where have I heard that before, although lately I'm not hearing it at all, at least not addressed to me.

OK, he's cute in a miniature kind of way; I'll grant that. And he can certainly work a room even though as near I can tell he isn't looking at anything particularly. And he draws waves of approval from burping, pooping and simply opening up his eyes in a way that suggests that humans set the charm bar considerably lower for their offspring than for their pets. Meanwhile everyone reacts as if he is doing everything for the first time, which while technically true, seems hardly sufficient reason for the chorus of huzzahs that has drowned out any mention or even memory of the good dog in the corner.

Not that I'm jealous. OK, maybe a little, you bet. It's just not that easy thinking you're the king of the hill and then all of a sudden being treated, well, like a dog. Of course I have nothing against infants. Heck, I was a puppy once and I know that the creator of all things goes out of his way to make newborns cute so their parents won't leave them at the curb.

Still, I doubt if I would have received the same reaction if I woke up the house at 3 a.m. or cried for no reason, or asked to be fed every three hours. I much preferred to be charming from the background; but with a baby, apparently there is no background. Wherever the baby is seems to be the center of things.

Maybe my issues come from being new at the baby game. By the time I arrived on the scene all the children had left the house (my mistress said the children didn't need a dog; they had sisters.) In fact, some people suggested that once the nest was empty, perhaps I was a replacement baby.

As if that were possible. I see that now. At the end of the day, I can be a good dog 'til the cows come home but I'll never be a good baby.

So I decided to do what everyone else was doing and just be amazed by the new life that stretched before me (honestly, he stretches a lot). I took to treating the baby as if he were the prince of England (which at least by association would make me the dog of the prince of England.) I graciously offered to lick his hand (a universal peace offering, although not always greeted with appropriate pomp) and then went into the next room and took a nap (always a good idea when disappointment strikes.)

In a few days, the baby will be gone and I'll be back to being top dog around the house until the next baby is carried or walks through the door.

And when someone calls me a "good dog", I'll remind myself that once a baby enters the room, even the best dog is still the second banana.

GUESTS

When Ben Franklin's dog famously observed that guests, like fish, begin to smell after three days, he probably didn't know the grave insult he was delivering.

To the fish.

Now of course there's nothing wrong with fish, even the three-day old variety which with minimal maintenance seem to be model houseguests. They arrive with their own watery accommodations often bringing their entourage of snails, seaweed and bubbling helmeted plastic divers; require only the flakiest of food (in fact the biggest danger seems to be overfeeding, a condition I am unacquainted with) and sit unobtrusively atop tables, never hogging (not that there's anything wrong with hogs) the conversation.

You would never see your basic fish attempt to push you off the sofa, nudge past you at the dinner bowl, or even think of disrupting your nap because he wanted to play.

The human objection that three-day old fish smell is just poppycock (not that there's anything wrong with poppies) all the more so coming from a species with perhaps the least developed olfactory system in the animal kingdom. It's like saying we smell doggy. What do they expect us to smell like – gardenias?

But just as I consider fish quite amiable houseguests, I cannot say the same for my own species. Bring a fellow canine into your home, even for a few days as happened to me recently, and it is as if the president of the United States just happened to pop in for a visit.

In my neck of the woods (a handsome neck if I say so myself), the passing of the summer solstice marks the official dawning of the summer guest-dog season. Suddenly, it seems to be raining dogs around here as humans pop in with pets in tow and then disappear for days at a time to places strangely unaccommodating to canines leaving me holding the doggy bag at home.

Now I'm an ordinary dog, but I find this perplexing, as the very nature of a dog is to supply rest and relaxation by the boatful and if I were considering a vacation (which I seldom do; home suits me just fine) my first requirement would be that any such spot be "dog friendly," a term I find a bit redundant since just about all dogs of my acquaintance are friendly when treated with even a modicum of simple decency.

You might suppose that dogs would realize what human houseguests should know, which is that a visitor's main function is to supply entertainment, evidence a somewhat wry but always engaging outlook and by all means minimize the disruption to the finely tuned workings of the household. And yet I find my canine guests seem to want to take over the place; insisting on walks and treats when they want them, jumping into my masters' bed (something I would never do), expropriating my toys, digging in my holes and, in general, distracting household members from the proper center of attention --- me.

Not that it bothers me (OK, maybe a little) when they nuzzle up to all comers insisting on being petted, stroked around the ears and shamelessly fishing (again, nothing wrong with fish) for that most coveted compliment of "good dog."

Well maybe and maybe not, but what really gets me when I overhear my masters saying that things seem to be working so well between the interloper and me that perhaps they would consider having two dogs in the house PERMANENTLY.

And that is certainly a dog fight for another day. For now, let me say that like many human hosts I am a bit less than heartbroken to see my dog guests go and have the operation of the house return to normal where there is no competition for best dog status. And should I ever get lonely for companionship after three days I can comfort myself with the thought that all things considered, I'd rather have a fish.

SIDEKICK

A little canine trivia for the New Year:

What do Rin Tin Tin, Lassie and Toto have in common?

Answer: They worked alone.

Sidekicks and straight men are great for human acts I suppose. Where would Laurel be without Hardy? Abbot without Costello? Penn without Teller? Humans need each other to take the falls, set up the punch lines and divert the audience so no one pays attention to the man behind the curtain, but I've seldom met a dog who didn't consider himself a lone wolf at heart. And while I don't claim to be good at math, I know enough doggy arithmetic to compute that one dog plus one dog is too many.

I am reminded of this after a busy holiday season of dogs dropping into my house like it was a bus station (a location which would never consider allowing dogs through the door.) To be sure, some of the canine interlopers were just there for the night under the mistaken notion that an invitation to share some holiday cheer might include them (I prefer to drink alone.) Others arrive dog toy and bowl in hand for the duration of the holidays while their owners decamp to places that would never think to allow dogs making me wonder if unbeknownst to me my masters had hung a doggy hotel sign outside the window with neon letters shouting "Vacancy."

Humbug.

I might be inclined to show some more holiday spirit about such company if my holiday visitors hadn't demonstrated such a remarkable ability to make themselves comfortable in what is obviously a one-dog home. Before I know it, they are invariably digging new holes in my yard (I like them just where I put them), dismembering my toys in ways I've never thought of, and nudging me away from my dinner as if they had never seen a dog bowl before.

All of which still wouldn't be so bad if they didn't hog (not that there's anything wrong with hogs, at least they eat outside) all the compliments that I have grown accustomed to as solo dog. I mean how after showing a few simple tricks (who cares if they can play dead, and what self-respecting dog would want to?) and flashing some big eyes can there all of a sudden be two "best dogs," in the house, as if that were even grammatically possible.

Then too there is the faint praise that wafts my way from those who say we play so well together, as if diplomacy were part of my job description coupled with the unwelcome observation aimed at no one in particular that it must be nice to have a dog around the house who does more than just sit around and nap.

As if that were a bad thing.

Ah well, why should humans be the only ones who are aggravated by house guests at this time of year? Soon enough I know the holidays will be over and the company will depart, leaving me once more as the one and only best dog.

Grammatically correct, and just as it's always been.

PROFESSOR

Not that anyone ever asked me, but I seem to have acquired a new position in my household:

Puppy professor.

This in addition to what I consider my primary and until now only job as "chief charmer," largely a ceremonial position whose only real responsibility is to sit quietly at the door and greet all comers as if they had returned from the 100 Years War even if they had just gone to the store for a bottle of milk, in return for which I would receive free room and board for life, limitless pats on the head, high praise for doing wildly ordinary things and the only title I (or any dog) ever cared about:

Good dog.

My new role started innocently enough (as all truly calamitous events do) when it was casually announced at the dinner table (a mostly congenial spot best suited for some artful begging) that a new puppy would be visiting for a while and it would be a perfect opportunity for me to "show him the ropes."

Now if I am in fact to be named professor -- like it or not -- let me parse that sentence a bit.

"New puppy," is of course redundant since puppies by their very nature are new and bring very few positive qualities to the table except of course another mouth to feed, and a certain kind of cuteness which seems genetically imprinted to newborns of all species largely to prevent their parents from throwing them out windows during extended bouts of early morning crying and near-constant pooping.

"Visiting for a while," is one of those charmingly vague human statements usually presented in the context of "I'll be back in a while" which is meant mostly to calm us down, but is of course completely meaningless to dogs who exist entirely in the present and whose notion of time doesn't extend far beyond knowing the approach of the dinner hour.

"Perfect opportunity" is a phrase which should be properly confined to that moment when humans have left food too close to the end of the table allowing us to "accidentally" knock it to the floor where we are all too glad to invoke the "five second rule" which doesn't exist for dogs, and which is wholly unnecessary as we have already devoured our just desserts in far less time than that.

And finally let us consider that delightful human idiom "show him the ropes," which literal minded canines might take to mean tie him up outside (a perfect place for puppies,) but which humans seem to think means showing him all the tricks of running things around the house without the humans noticing and in so doing put myself right out of my job.

But perhaps that is where I should start my first lesson, which is that we're not in charge around here. And if I am to be a puppy professor, however reluctantly, I might as well get right to it, so as to make a "little while" come somewhat sooner (whatever that means) and return to the days of chief (and only) charmer as soon as possible.

And so began my days as Obiwan Kadoggie with my new charge literally at my heels following me around the house, through the park, into the backyard and on road trips, where I showed him the fine canine arts of chasing (but never catching) squirrels, digging for voles (a personal favorite), doing our "business" (it's not exactly wall-street arbitrage) and sticking our heads out the car window to feel the wind in our face and the world passing by. Advanced coursework included approaching other dogs (carefully), small children (curiously), dismembering stuffed dog toys (exuberantly), and chasing our tails (pointless, but fun).

I must say that in short order we cut a dashing figure together out on the town, with the only drawback being that on occasion passersby would stop in their tracks and remark aloud that they had never seen a dog so cute and playful.

And they wouldn't mean me.

And so the master has become the student, as I have noticed myself cavorting more vigorously, playing more intensely, digging more gustily and jumping into my master's lap in ways I haven't done in years, trying to keep up with all the new doggish energy in the house and admitting to myself that despite a certain canine proverb, you CAN teach an old dog new tricks -- if you bring a young one into the house.

I guess that despite my initial misgivings, there are some ropes that remain to be shown and maybe it might not be so bad if the "little while" that remained in my tenure before I become puppy professor emeritus lasted just a little while longer.

KITCHEN

There's been quite a commotion around my house this summer as a seemingly endless number of craftsmen go about the somewhat curious task of remodeling our kitchen.

Now generally, I take a welcoming attitude toward whomever walks through our doors. Human guests are invariably given the royal treatment with a full wag and swagger, while fellow canines are politely shown around the premises with a "micasa es su casa" nod to make themselves at home.

Even lowlier life forms such as a small field mouse scampering across the bathroom floor draw a live-and-let-live reaction, hardly the response of my mistress followed by her crazed (to my mind) suggestion that maybe what this house needed was a c-a-t.! But this new parade of workers was a horse of a different color (nothing wrong with that). Instead of the polite conversation and spot of tea that awaited most guests, this army proceeded ant-like (nothing wrong with ants) to start tearing up the place amid promises of a spanking new kitchen the likes of which had never been seen before.

Not that there was anything wrong with the old kitchen that I could see. I mean it hadn't been struck by lightning or hit by a tree. In fairness I suppose I should add that I am not a great judge of kitchens as frankly, I have never seen their point.

After all, for my entire life my food has arrived out of a bag, uncooked, unrefrigerated in a single dish that hardly ever saw the inside of dishwasher, so that just about all kitchen appliances would be largely wasted on me. Nor did I understand the pronouncement that the shelves and cabinetry appeared "tired" (whatever that means) and due for an "upgrade," an opinion that I secretly feared might someday be applied to me.

Nevertheless, I don't exactly call the shots around here and, hence, the daily procession of carpenters, painters, electricians and plumbers tramping (nothing wrong with tramping) through the house, each promising to beautify the

place but leaving a trail of dust and debris in an effort to do so.

I, of course, remained ever gracious, welcoming these strangers, accepting the usual good dog compliments (they seemed to be a dog-friendly crew) and then stepping out of the way as they went about their mayhem. And sure enough, out of the seeming rubble a new and presumably less tired kitchen began to appear.

I can now say that after several weeks of displacement, my new kitchen is the pride and joy of my mistress and the envy of human visitors (canines remain understandably less impressed) who go about the odd ritual of opening and closing cabinets, dishwashers and refrigerator doors to no apparent purpose other than they can, and showering them with high praise usually reserved for well, me.

My meals continue to arrive in the usual way in my one largely unwashed dish (not that I'm complaining) and life appears to have returned to somewhat normal with the army of workers decamping to other battlefields where they are presumably tearing down walls and ripping up floors with the promise of future invigoration.

I must say that in the way of most guests I was happy to see them coming and less than heartbroken to see them go. Perhaps one day they will be invited like true guests to see the fruits of their labors and stay for a spot of tea. They can leave their tools at home.

WEDDING

There was a wedding in my family recently and I'd like to say that the bride was radiant and the groom dashing, but I must admit sheepishly (or is that, doggishly) that I don't really know, because I wasn't really there. Because I wasn't really invited.

There, I've said it, not that it lessens the sting (and I've been stung before, who knew that bees would be so sensitive — but that hornet's nest is a different can of worms).

And now I'm mixing metaphors which is what I do when I get upset, which I'm proud to say is rarely. But not being invited to a family wedding?

Really?

After all the talk about how I'm a member of the family, and that the family wouldn't be the same without me and that I've made the family complete, I guess we'll have to add an asterisk.

* Except for weddings.

Not that I would have insisted on an actual engraved invite. After all, those things are expensive and technically, I can't read, or for that matter open an envelope except with my teeth, after which there wouldn't be much to read anyway.

But the point is that it would have been nice to be asked, instead of simply being left home to stand guard (over what? My dashed hopes?) while the rest of the family marched down the aisle to the Canon in D(og) which anyone knows was written by Pachelbel's dog (why else does the song sound like it's chasing its tail?.

Surely there must have been some role for me to play, especially as this was an outdoor wedding and I am an outdoor kind of dog. Perhaps ring bearer would have been a stretch considering my propensity to: a) run away with things and just drop them in the woods, or b) swallow them, which is just a mess all around.

But I love to greet guests and been told that I am a pretty good dancer for a dog, (especially compared to my master who doesn't have the excuse of having four legs.) I don't drink too much (and when I do it's just water) and I seldom think of family celebrations as dandy occasions to rehash grievances that happened 20 years ago. I don't flirt with anyone else's wife. And when I get tired of someone's company, I simply crawl under a table and nap, which is a lot better manners than many wedding guests have been known to display.

All in all, I think that any fair- minded observer would agree that so far as celebrants go, my behavior would rate in the above average range yet I am left behind because — and there is no nice way to say this — I'm a dog.

But fortunately, a forgiving one.

So when the guests stumbled in after what by all accounts was a gala evening, I greeted them with my usual enthusiasm as if they deserved the Nobel prize for just walking through the door, and acted as if they had done me a great favor by telling me they would be back soon, which as any dog knows is a phrase with no actual canine translation.

For us, it's always now, or *not* now.

I slobbered my enthusiasm and stole a bite of left-over cake, which I figured was modest recompense considering the social insult I had endured and I remained charming long after the last hanger-on had departed. And when my master bragged that I was just like one of the family I didn't even growl.

Just see who I invite to my wedding.

A DOG
FOR ALL SEASONS

YEAR of THE DOG

Chalk it up to our rather casual relationship to time, but dogs don't care much for calendars, and I suspect that humans would not be so keen on them either if each time the earth finished a trip around the sun they found themselves seven years older.

And this whole one-year-for-you-equals-seven-years for me business makes it hard even to imagine a true dog calendar (I'm not talking about the ones you see at mall kiosks where each month features a cute dog cavorting through the seasons) I mean technically such a true calendar would need 84 months (12 times 7 for arithmetic challenged readers) and just what would these months be called. Dogcember of course, but after that your average dog would just lose interest, leaving the rest of the months nameless, or simply DogcemberA, but then again what happens beyond Z.

The whole thing is just too confusing and better left to humans who seem to care inordinately about such things as the passage of time. So imagine my surprise to discover, thanks to a takeout menu from from a nearby Chinese restaurant (I love Chinese food), that February 16 will mark the official beginning of the Year of Dog.

Well happy New Year to me.

Now I would have thought that a dog's new year's celebrations would be a quiet affair. After all we don't drink champagne, and look plain silly wearing funny hats. We rarely stay up to midnight (we prefer to beauty sleep) and if a ball (even a 2-ton one) dropped in front of us, we'd more likely chase it than wait for it to get to bottom and start kissing everything in sight.

And yet, I was to learn that if I expected dog new years to be a solitary and somewhat unheralded event I would be barking up the wrong tree.

While the approach of the year of the dog was going pretty much unnoticed around my neck of the woods, more than 1 million people in South Korea got a jump start on celebrations (not that there's anything wrong with jump starts) by gathering at the Bosingak Bell last year to ring in their hopes and dreams for the coming year.

While regrettably I could not be there for the Korean pre-party (I don't fly) some quick Internet research (courtesy of my master – at least he's good for something) revealed that the Year of the Dog is part of a repeating 12-year cycle which assigns to the calendar twelve Zodiac animals, the rat, ox, tiger, rabbit, dragon, snake, horse, goat, monkey, rooster, dog and pig.

The story goes that once upon a time, the Jade Emperor summoned all animals on the planet, decreeing that the years of the calendar would be named after each animal in the order they arrived to greet him. The rat came in first place by hitching a ride on the ox's back. The ox and tiger came in second and third by virtue of their natural strength.

The rabbit arrived fourth by jumping from one stone to another. The dragon, in spite of its ability to fly, came in fifth as it had to stop and make rain to help all the creatures on earth. The horse and snake came in at the same time, but the snake's sudden appearance frightened the horse to pass the snake, which came in sixth. The goat, monkey, and rooster came in side by side by helping each other swim through the river. The dog and pig arrived last.

Tied for *last*? Say what?

Now since by some reckonings the Jade Emperor is 200 million years old (over a billion in dog time) perhaps some of the story got lost in translation, and while I could see finishing behind a tiger or a rabbit, I can't imagine losing any kind of fair contest to a rat, a goat or a rooster, much less an ox. And a snake. Seriously?

Be that as it may, I am thrilled to see that we are now entering the Year of the Dog which by all accounts seems to be full of surprises.

People born in the Year of the Dog are said to be loyal, honest, and confident (natch) but at times selfish, stubborn, and eccentric (possible, I suppose).

Three former presidents of the United States were born in the Year of the Dog including Bill Clinton, George W. Bush and you know who; along with Mother Theresa, Benjamin Franklin, Elvis Presley, Michael Jackson, Justin Bieber, and Madonna, which proves only that people, like dogs, are a mixed breed.

Alert readers might also be interested to know that my lucky numbers are 3, 4, and 9, (lottery hounds take note); my lucky colors are red and green; my lucky flowers are roses, cymbidium, and orchids and my lucky direction is south. My unlucky numbers are 1,6, and 7. My unlucky direction is southeast (what kind of direction is that?) and my unlucky colors are blue, white, and get this…gold.

Gold ? Really? So what is a golden retriever to do in the Year of the Dog?

Follow my nose, smell the roses, and beg for Chinese food every chance I get.

Happy dog new year.

WINTER

Every time the snow starts falling in those big heavy bunches that makes the trees bend and make me feel like I am in the middle of one those human snow globes (like the one with a mermaid trapped inside -- hey, I'm only a dog and even I know that's fishy) it reminds me that I am a dog for all seasons.

Oh sure, I love the fall and chasing through the leaves that just happen to be my favorite color (golden of course) which one would think would provide a natural camouflage for squirrel chasing (they don't). And sure I have a warm spot for those summer dog days of stretching out on the front porch, begging for bits of hamburger dropped from an outdoor grill.

Of course there is spring when the woods come to life again, bringing out hibernating voles, chipmunks and other woodland creatures for me to… *play* with.

But one of the nice things about being blessed with a short memory (besides making it nearly impossible to hold a grudge) is that each season arrives anew. For a dog, there is no winter of discontent, only new possibilities and if as the poet Robert Frost (guess his favorite season) remarks there are miles to go before we sleep, we dogs know that's a good thing.

And so even as I am glad that I am not a Chicago dog where winter arrives routinely like a bad houseguest too early and stays too late, I welcomed the polar vortex that snapped across New England recently as a chance to reacquaint myself with the joys of winter and remind myself that good things often come in white-out packages.

No sooner had the worst of the snow died down, I was nudging my master for some winter fun in the woods, sliding along icy streams, cavorting through high drifts and boldly going where chattering humans dared not go, over frozen hill and dale (even though I'm a bit foggy on just what a dale is.)

Oddly, (a phrase that increasingly comes to mind when dealing with humans) for all the talk about winter wonderland and holiday sleigh rides to grandmother's house (most of the grandmothers I know live in Florida) humans seem to most enjoy the outdoors largely by staying inside and viewing it through insulated glass windows.

My own master, for example, needs to be repeatedly cajoled into taking me out (don't worry I'm up for the job) and for reasons unknown keeps reminding me to "do my business" in haste so that we (meaning he) can as soon as possible return to the hearth (sadly, a figure of speech, we don't really have a hearth, a situation I would remedy if I were ever placed in charge of home remodeling here.)

All of which makes it increasingly clear that he has no idea of what my "business" is, since as any canine can tell you the "business" of being a dog is to have fun regardless of the outside temperature.

Instead, my shivering master is acting like a grumpy lion in winter, except that all the lions of my acquaintance are actually even tempered about the cold (a situation that likely arises from never actually ever having to face it).

Still, that's how it is with humans. Just when you think you have them figured, you don't. When summer comes they complain about being too hot; then comes winter and they're complaining about the cold.

Need I remind them that they're not the ones running around barefoot and naked?

About the only redeeming trait of humans complaining about the weather is that even after the most frigid cold snap ,it only takes a few days of increasing temperatures to warm their hearts. A few days of melting and they're actually convinced that mud is OK (actually it's not that bad once you roll in it) and they've completely forgotten about the near Arctic temperatures that kept them indoors the previous week.

Before you know it they'll be singing the joys of spring awakening which will last all of a few minutes before they remember.

Here comes hayfever.

WINTER AGAIN

Loyal readers of my column may recall that I have previously said that although I like to think of myself as dog for all seasons, the truth is that I loved fall the best.

Well the truth is that was when fall, was well, *fall*. But now it's winter and I've discovered a new truth, one that is more in keeping with my doglike nature -- that truth isn't something you can bottle up and put on a shelf and then take it down and just look at it forever. It's more like a cloud that looks like a rabbit the first time you lift your head, and then when you shake your head a second later it looks like a duck. Rabbit, or duck?

The truth is, it depends.

Which is my roundabout way of saying that now that the snows have fallen, I find that I like winter the best. Sure fall was great when I was romping through the leaves and admiring the way the wind painted the woods my favorite color which of course was golden. And I admit I may have favored the fall a bit at the time because it offered the hope of thinning camouflage for squirrels with the autumnal promise that I might catch one when the days grew short.

But of course I didn't. And it's beginning to look like the trees could be bare year around and my master could outfit me with infrared goggles and any sporting fellow would still handicap the squirrel 3-to-1 and he'd be right. And the more I go through the seasons I have to admit that fall *was* my favorite season because it was fall, but now that it's winter, it's winter. Dogs are like that. Never trust us to answer a question about our favorites because the truth is – and this is the ultimate dog truth – *everything* is our favorite.

It's what makes us so doggish.

But back to winter. Can anything match a romp through six foot high drifts that cover up the trails where the leaves are but a memory, and dogs don't really do memory very well. Or the sheer excitement of catching the scent of a

hibernating vole who thinks he is safe just because he can't be seen? Can there be anything more relaxing than unearthing a stick from underneath a pile of fresh fallen snow and then chewing on it for hours while wondering how it is that snow falls down and not stay up?

Well can there?

I say no. And if it were true at the time that fall was my favorite then, is it any less true than winter is my favorite now. Or is it perhaps more true (a philosophical quagmire if ever I heard one) as Ralph Waldo Emerson's dog once said that a foolish consistency is the hobgoblin of little minds. Now I suppose that is a question best left to hobgoblins, but in the meantime I say, "let it snow."

The nice thing about being a dog is that you get all the joys of winter without any of the human hassles that seem to accompany the season. For example did you ever see a dog with a snow brush or ice scraper asking himself why he doesn't live in Florida? I doubt it. Or a dog looking at three feet of freshly fallen snow and thinking to himself that the first thing he has to do is shovel it away?

Of course not.

Or a dog fighting with his wife about whether he should turn up the heat, or she should get a sweater. That is silly on so many levels that even a dog wouldn't answer.

No, for us ice scrapers are for chewing when sticks can't be found. Snow is for romping and since we spend our time on all fours, we never fall. As for snow removal, well isn't that what the sun is for? And for the grand sweater/vs heat debate; don't make us laugh.

Just about the only drawback to snow is that sometimes I have to remind my master that it's time to go out even if he'd rather stay home. But isn't that why God made us charming and never burdened us with indoor plumbing?

As for that consistency thing, remind me to ask the next hobgoblin I meet in the snowy woods with the thick flakes falling on my warm nose. And if I don't meet one until spring then I can ask him why spring is my favorite season.

Which I am sure it will be.

All in due time.

BEACH

Due to an unfortunate combination of weather forecasts (why do humans pay so much attention to these things, we dogs just say let's go) and my master's mid-July hip replacement (I should be more understanding, I expect future hip problems of my own) I hardly got to the beach at all this summer and if dogs could get grumpy, I would be.

Oh all right, maybe I am just a little. It's just that I love the beach (of course I love just about everything) and although dogs are incapable of irony and with our limited vocabulary tend to avoid double entendres, I've come to embrace the human slogan "Life's a Beach" even though I suspect that somewhere it contains a slur against dogs.

It's just that the beach represents everything dogs love most -- open spaces, the sand beneath our feet and the lure of the water inviting us to come play.

I remember my first days at the beach. I was only a pup of course but I knew that I was in store for a treat when we pulled up to ocean's edge and my master said "go play," which next to "it's supper time," is music to a dog's ears.

I confess to an initial fear of the ocean which I admit I approached tentatively putting just my front feet into the surf and then strategically retreating like a sandpiper when the waves came in. But then my breeding took over (we weren't born with webbed feet for nothing) and before long I was frolicking in the waves leading me to believe that somewhere along the evolutionary line there had to be some dogfish in my family tree.

And I was pleasantly surprised at how naturally the dog paddle came to me, yet another example of how nature had compensated for my lack of an opposable thumb with four coordinated legs that made me practically amphibious in a way that turns most humans green with envy (although if humans were totally honest they would be green with envy at a dog's life most of the time.)

And I was even happier to learn that thanks to a drip-dry coat of fur and a superior circulatory system the cold water didn't bother me at all, meaning that not only is there no namby-pamby tiptoeing into the water that humans are so fond of but that I find I can go fall swimming even in Maine (Maine's state motto: the water is great but no one goes in) when even the whales have headed south for warmer weather.

Of course since I'm a dog and my transportation options are limited, I'm pretty much dependent on the kindness of strangers to get me to the beach and July and August just flew by before I realized that I had been beach-deprived pretty much all summer. In addition to my master's hip replacement there was the arrival of a new grand-baby that just about put all beach plans on hold (just because human babies can't swim I don't see why I should suffer). Add a few hurricanes and some pesky shark sightings on Cape Cod and the habit of some beach communities to legislate dogs away from the water to make room for more humans (things will be different when dogs rule the world) and before I knew it Labor Day had arrived with my fur still bone dry (not that there's anything wrong with bones – yum).

Luckily September beaching favors dogs. Tourists go home, kids go back to school, and even the snobbiest shore communities become more tolerant of seeing us in the waves. And as cold water doesn't bother us a bit (why is it that the same humans who won't step a foot into water less than 70 degrees will willingly dump a bucket of ice water on their heads?) we pretty much have the beach to ourselves.

And so I have hope that as the leaves begin to turn and a chill takes over the night air, there will still be some time to get to the beach just a few more times before winter.

Life can be a beach all right but sometimes the best thing to do when life gets too "beachy" is to jump right in.

VACATIONS

It's vacation time around here once again, and I am in the humiliating position (actually, dogs don't get humiliated; ask one who's spent the day rolling in the mud) of reminding the humans who share my humble digs (nothing wrong with digging) of an axiomatic truth surrounding summer's doggish days.

Vacations, c'est moi.

Not that I actually need a vacation of course as just about any way you look at it, a dog's life is pretty much a permanent vacation.

After all, I don't punch a clock (although I've chewed on a few) and I've never paid for a meal (or anything else.) I wake up whenever I please and I spend much of my day napping. I stay away from cable tv news, presidential tweets (a bird-brain idea), and if you don't count the rather minor annoyance of the cat next door and the ever-elusive squirrel outside my window, my life is practically stress free.

Nor do I have a desire to see the world and visit far-off places. I've always believed that if the maker of all things had meant dogs to fly, he/she (we are ecumenical on this subject) would have given us wings. And then there is the blatant dog-ism of airports (sure we're good enough to sniff out drug dealers and miscreants in security lines but try climbing aboard an actual plane and they treat you like a terrorist.)

Despite the stories you've heard about dogs traveling miles to reunite with their masters, we are mostly homebodies. Wanderlust rarely takes me beyond walking distance. From a dog's eye view, if you've seen one forest you've pretty much seen them all. Museums and churches leave me cold, and most of them won't allow me inside anyway.

No, it's not the vacation venues I miss; it's the company.

For the life of me I can't understand why anyone would want to leave me home. For years, family vacations were taken without me despite the tearful exchanges at separation (theirs not mine; I have a stiff upper lip, the better to snack by) and the obvious (to me) value-added of taking me along. Even my most pathetic gesture of sitting in an empty suitcase as my humans were packing wasn't enough to unstiffen their resolve and my best googly eyes failed to spark even a simple google search of dog-friendly accommodations. And the less said about the k-e-n-n-e-l (I like to spell so the thought doesn't enter their heads) the better.

Unexpectedly what sealed (nothing wrong with seals) the deal was a road trip to a fellow dog lover's home where at every rest stop along the way, my masters encountered sad eyed travelers wishing to pet me (I never say no) and express-ing the fervent wish that they had taken their dog along on their vacations (as if I could do something about that).

With that epiphany, any thoughts of another summer in a drafty European cathedral, or a stuffy post-modern museum (whatever that means) simply drift-ed away amid their promise that each summer beach vacation would include moi.

No more googly eyes; no dog-occupied suitcase, no tearful goodbyes and no fear of the word that rhymes with fennel.

Just the unassailable logic that a vacation without the family dog was no vacation at all.

And so it was a wonderful week of swimming, cavorting, and frolicking at the shore along with a generous portion of petting from complete stranger vaca-tioners who wish they had taken their dogs on vacation.

Will they never learn?

For a species that likes to think they run the world, humans are sometimes not too bright.

But then again, I've suspected that.

Thanksgiving

With the passing of Thanksgiving (thank goodness) it's full blown holiday season among the humans in my household and all I have to say is *humbug.*

Not that there's anything wrong with humbugs which most human etymologists deny is even a bug at all, tracing its origins to the 18th century city of Hamburg (yum) where counterfeiting seems to have been the main industry. Most canine entomologists (what a difference an "N" makes) prefer to think the word descends from a "humming bug", the song of which continues to be elusive to most human scientists but which can be heard quite easily if your ears are good enough by dogs on routine walks through the woods.

Where was I before I got sidetracked (nothing wrong with that) by the siren sounds of humbugs in woods? Oh yes, human holidays which are rarely celebrated in the woods surrounded by humbugs, but by an infestation of guests walking right up to my door wishing all sorts of good cheer even as they are increasingly underfoot (particularly annoying when you have four feet) and staying long past when they have outworn their welcome.

Holiday season for humans begins with Halloween, which by the calendar should arrive well after the leaves change, but which thanks to human marketing actually falls well before fall, shortly after school starts, giving young children a sugar high even without the sugar as they imagine an evening of ghosts, pirates, and witches (surprisingly few dress up as dogs) who arrive carrying the vague threat of tricks (do they intend to roll over or play dead) and rewarded by enough candy to kill them.

Still, Halloween has its good points. For one it is celebrated almost entirely by children, (the best of the bunch as humans go) eager to pet me at the door, and fawn (nothing wrong with fawns) over my beauty (oh, shucks). And after being bought off with nominal treats (nothing compared with a tasty butcher bone) they leave without actually crossing the threshold.

The same can hardly be said for Thanksgiving which is pretty much an endless parade of guests stepping into my house, hogging (nothing wrong with hogs) the best spots on the sofa, and simply sticking around until all the food is gone. And while there appears to be great lip service to the notion of gratitude at the start of the meal much of the conversation around the table seems to be a rehash (nothing wrong with hash) of old family feuds and overheated (and pointless) political discussions which most dogs couldn't care less about until dinner arrives reminding us mostly to be thankful for leftovers, and more importantly, that we are not turkeys.

Which brings us to Christmas, or Hannukah or Kwanza (we canines are an ecumenical lot) where humans go to great lengths proclaiming the goals of peace, love and good will toward man, seemingly forgetting that *they* are in charge around here and that perhaps changing the world for the better might require a tiny bit more effort than lighting a few candles, bringing a tree indoors (what's with that?), and giving each other presents.

And then before you know it, the year is gone, along with the leftovers, the guests, the out-of-its-element tree, and the good intentions, at least bringing a bit more peace and quiet to my house as I reflect on another year (or in my limited lifetime, seven years) shot.

It's all enough to send any dog straight to the woods longing for the sweet sounds of the glorious humbug.

CALENDAR

One of the great things about being a dog (and face it, it's all great) is that every day is Sunday, which makes the notion of a dog calendar sort of a hoot.

Not that I have anything against hoots (some of my best friends are hooters, and I mean that in the purely Strigiformes, non-lecherous way.) The point is that giving a dog a calendar is like giving a fish an umbrella - the thought may be sweet, but what on earth would he use it for.

I have long noted that it's not exactly true that dogs can't tell time. We know when it's time to eat, time to go out and time for bed, and really how much more is there to tell.

It's more like we don't let time tell us. There's a very good reason that Lewis Carroll's dog would never populate Wonderland with a dog saying "I'm late" because no rabbit would believe it.

We move in our own sweet time which has nothing whatsoever to do with tax deadlines, religious holidays, or presidential birthdays. We're never too busy to stop and smell the roses, because we stop and smell everything. We view the seasons with equanimity finding winter every bit as joyous as summer (and with fewer ticks) and recognize that Labor Day and Independence Day are somewhat pointless for a species that never works and revels in its pet status. In short, the only reason that human calendars don't simply mark every day as Dog Day is that (as our mothers told us) every day IS dog day.

And yet each year mall kiosks, stationery stores, and most of the Internet is lousy with dog calendars (not that I have anything against louses, who quite possibly have worse reputations than ticks.) It seems that four-color dogs are everywhere, racing through leaves in October, leaping over snow drifts in December, parading through the flowers in May, lolling by a stream in August, and cavorting through all the rest of the months as if there were no tomorrow;

which while true from our perspective sort of defeats the purpose of a calendar in so many ways.

Not that any of this foolishness stops humans from buying dog calendars and presenting them to each other as the days grow short.

In my neighborhood (and I am not making this up), an august member of the legal community who should certainly know something about months arrives each December like Santa Claus (don't get me started, except for the flying reindeer, nothing about that old gent smells believable) toting a spanking new Golden Retriever calendar which bears a striking resemblance to the old one except some numbers have been changed in the part that has nothing to do with dogs.

The rest (by which I mean most interesting part) of the calendar shows us doing the same leaping, frolicking, swimming, and dashing through the woods, fields and months that took up all of last year until we once again collapse in something of a lump (although a cute lump) before a roaring fire sometime in late December.

Do they never learn? We don't care what day, or month or year it is. Humans would have better luck asking their fish to borrow his umbrella.

I guess the best that can be said of this particular piece of foolishness is that such calendars sometimes raise money for worthy (by which I mean canine) causes and that humans buy them for the same reason that they buy calendars showing timeless scenes of grand canyons, majestic mountains and blooming flowers.

It gives them something to smile about in the darkest hours. And what dog could be against that?

Reilly Chipkin born Nov. 16, 2019

AND THEN CAME REILLY

Despite countless dog shows to the contrary, if there's one thing a dog knows, it's that you can't compete with another dog.

Especially a dog that's now of blessed memory.

Which is exactly the circumstance I found myself in when I took up residence last year in the home previously occupied by Theo.

Not that I couldn't see what I was getting into (I seldom miss much around here, and after all, getting into things is pretty much what puppies do.)

There were signs of Theo everywhere. Beyond the seemingly endless cute photos of my predecessor throughout the years, (doesn't anyone take pictures of their dogs being bad?) there was Theo's dog bed, a matched set of Theo food bowls, a large selection of half chewed dog toys (sans bladders, -- I was too polite to ask), Theo coffee mugs (I prefer tea, hold the tea bag), and -- get this, -- a fossilized plaster of Paris pawprint on his final day, all to serve as reminders (as if anyone could forget) about who he was, and who would likely remain top dog in the house.

Still, I recognized my responsibility to do something to lift the general gloom that had descended around the place since Theo's passing, a task I jumped into (nothing wrong with jumping) with puppy-like enthusiasm, doing my best to leave my mark on the place (occasionally rather unhygienically) and letting all who entered know that there was indeed a new dog in town.

And if I must say so myself (who else is going to say it?) as much as such a thing is possible, it kind of worked. Before long and after a few trips to the pet store (where dogs are not only allowed but downright welcomed) the house began to fill up with my own puppy crate, (thankfully they never called it a cage); my own dog dish, and my own soon-to-be dismembered toys, all of which gave the house a decidedly doggish feel which along with my polite importuning to

go for a walk on a regular basis gave my bereaved humans something
to do besides sit around and remember what it was like when they used to
have a dog.

Because here I am. And while I would never presume to replace Theo
(canines know that each of us is "sui generis", which is just dog Latin for one
of a kind) I never thought I was replacing Theo; only that I was replacing the
dark cloud that had enveloped the place - a task I like to think that Theo, and
all dogs pretty much live for.

Nor does it bother me, -- as I hear that it can annoy new girlfriends, middle
children and freshly encountered high school acquaintances, to occasionally
be called by the wrong name, my response to which is to energetically (I am
ever-energetic) respond to all doggy sounding names such as butch, pup, doggy.

And especially, Theo.

Of course I am not above learning a few doggy tricks of my own in hopes of
putting my own paw print on the place and earning the highest of dog praise.

"Good dog."

Which, with a few modest exceptions I like to think is true, and which I especially like to think would have made Theo proud.